The Astrology Workbook

How to Interpret your Natal Chart

By Wade Coleman

July 2020 edition

Upon my death, this book enters the Public Domain

Table of Contents

Forward

For the beginner, reading your natal chart is intimidating. This book is a step by step checklist of the techniques I use when reading a chart. This is a workbook and not a textbook.

The text for the workbook is *The Only Way to Learn Astrology* (Volume 1-3) by Marion Mach and Joan McEvers. There are other good books on astrology, but this text was my first, and I like the series.

My first astrology class was in a used book store with half a dozen students. People would drop in for a class, and the students would discuss the native's chart.

But the real lesson began when we stopped talking, and we let natives talk about their life experience, and we relate the information to their chart. From these classes, I made an astounding discovery that not everyone thought and communicated like me, an Aquarius, a Fixed Air sign.

I always wondered why do people get so upset over receiving information? It's just facts. Then I studied astrology and discovered that Water signs communicate with emotions. Fire signs are usually fearless and outspoken, while Earth signs are more reserved. Air signs are generally abstract thinkers. This gem of information improved my interpersonal skills.

Astrology and Gender

Planets and astrological signs have gender. I refer to Venus and the Moon as *she* and Sun, Mars, and Jupiter as *he*. Mercury is a hermaphrodite. He changes gender depending on the sign he/she occupies.

Print Edition

Before you begin reading have pencils, and colored pens nearby. There is something magical about writing things down to fix facts into your memory. There are many tables to fill out, so copy them and fill out each block. This will help you memorize the symbols for planets and astrological signs.

I choice to print the book in color because it helps the mind organize facts. I know it cost more, but color helps the learning process.

Chapter 1

Element and Qualities

The zodiac are constellations that encircle the earth along the ecliptic (the path of the sun through the sky). They are the channels through which universal energies, symbolized by planets, flow. These forces manifest through human activity. Therefore, signs represent the way we go about being and doing.

The twelve signs are part of us in various degrees of emphasis. They are composed of four elements (Fire, Water, Air, and Earth) and three modalities (Cardinal, Fixed, and Mutable).

	Sign		Element	Modality
1	Aries	♈	Fire	Cardinal
2	Taurus	♉	Earth	Fixed
3	Gemini	♊	Air	Mutable
4	Cancer	♋	Water	Cardinal
5	Leo	♌	Fire	Fixed
6	Virgo	♍	Earth	Mutable
7	Libra	♎	Air	Cardinal
8	Scorpio	♏	Water	Fixed
9	Sagittarius	♐	Fire	Mutable
10	Capricorn	♑	Earth	Cardinal
11	Aquarius	♒	Air	Fixed
12	Pisces	♓	Water	Mutable

The Modalities

Cardinal

The *Cardinal* modality *initiates action* in a definite direction. Cardinal signs deal with change; they build momentum and generating power towards intense life experiences.

The cardinal signs are Aries, Cancer, Libra, and Capricorn.

Keywords: Initiate action.

Fixed

The *Fixed* modality *concentrate and focuses energy*. It provides definitions and structures. The fixed signs give depth and meaning to the cardinal experience. The fixed modality represent concentrated energy gathered inward toward a center or radiating outward from a center.

The fixed signs are Taurus, Leo, Scorpio, and Aquarius.

Keywords: security, stability, and intensity.

Mutable

The *Mutable* modality symbolizes the principle of *flexibility and adaptation*. It distributes the energy that has been concentrated and released by the fixed mode. The mutable modality combines and integrates the cardinal and fixed modes within itself. Mutable deals with constant change.

The Mutable signs are Gemini, Virgo, Sagittarius, and Pisces.

Keywords: adaptable. Changeable. Assimilation & transmission. Learning & Teaching.

The Elements

The elements in astrology are not the same as the periodic chart of elements in modern chemistry.

The classic four elements are more like to the four states of matter.

Fire – Plasma

Water – Liquids

Air – Gasses

Earth – Solid Matter

These elements are universal and manifest in all forms. When they manifest in human personality, they take on these attributes.

Element	Symbol	Attributes
Fire	△	Spontaneous. Reactive. Impulsive. Fearless. Courageous. Assertive. Identity issues.
Water	▽	Fluid. Emotional. Intuitive. Emotional issues.
Air	△	Intellectual. Detached. Communicative. Social. Social and intellectual issues.
Earth	▽	Practical. Pragmatic. Cautious. Sensual. Practical issues.

Fire

Fire signs (Aries, Leo, and Sagittarius) are considered positive, masculine, or initiating signs.

Fire is associated with the vernal equinox, the beginning of cyclic activity in the springtime. Fire is the vital life force; in astrological symbolism, it represents the principle of animation, vitality, and action. Fire signs express the warming, energizing life principle as enthusiasm, faith, encouragement, and the drive to express self.

Fire signs are impulsive. They and have pride, passion, courage, and creativity. Fire is difficult to contain and is guided by spirit. Fire signs often take the lead and are idealists. Aries initiates and are brave and enthusiastic innovators. Aries is more concerned about the present and future than the past. Leo is a Fixed Fire sign that is passionate, loyal, and makes a good manager. Sagittarius is a Mutable Fire sign that is more adaptable and flexible than the other Fire signs.

Fire is hot (expansive) and dry (destructive) and breaks down and consumes the forms through which it becomes manifest. Psychologically this can manifest in an individual as impatient and destructive behavior. The Book of Tokens says that destruction is the foundation of existence. Therefore, destruction is fundamental for renewal.

Fire Attributes

Identity issues. Strength of will. The originating principle of all activity. Enthusiasm. Vitality. Faith. Encouragement. Strength of will. Courageous. Generous. Altruism. Intuition. The drive to express self.

Water

Cancer, Scorpio, and Pisces are water signs. Water is considered negative, feminine, or receptive. Water signs express sensitivity, feelings, and empathy with others. Water refers to sensory, emotional, and creative life experiences.

Water is associated with the summer solstice when the forces of Life are at its strongest. The Water element is the primordial substance from which all things are formed. It has been called the root-matter, astral fluid, mental energy, or electromagnetic energy. The circulation and condensation of this energy produce physical manifestation.

Water signs rely more on their senses than logic. They're nurturing, perceptive, psychic, and understanding. Cancer is emotional, focused on home and family. Scorpio has deep desires, motivations, and needs intimate connections. Pisces is exceptionally compassionate and impressionable.

Water signs, along with Earth signs, belong to the feminine, yin, or receptive signs. They are often private and led by their feelings and feel their way through a situation. Water signs seek the deeper meaning of things and are healers.

The element Water, as expressed through the individual manifests as sensitivity, feelings, and empathy with others, nurturing, loving, and giving. It refers to sensory, emotional, and creative life experiences.

Water Attributes

The principle of universality. Feelings. Soul concerns. Memory and Imagination. The emotional plane of human activity. Love. Nurturing. Life-sustaining.

Air

Gemini, Libra, and Aquarius are air signs. Air signs are considered positive, masculine, or initiating signs.

Air is associated with the autumn equinox when the forces of life and consciousness are equal. Air signs are related to the mind's sensations, perception and expression, and abstract ideas.

Air refers to life experiences that involve adaptation and the use of the intellect. In a broader sense, it signifies wisdom, clarity, cleanliness, intelligence, reason, the ability to communicate, and the expansion of being. It is collective (inclusive) in nature.

Element Air is gaseous and volatile. The principle of air has the quality of warmth (expansion) from the Fire principle and that of humidity (mental substance) from Water. It is the medium between Fire and Water. Air is the agency through which the power of the solar rays of the sun is carried to earth.

Air signs are humanitarian, intellectual, social, and communicative. Gemini (mutable air) is the most adaptable of the Air signs. It takes a mental approach to life, sorting, repatterning, and distributing ideas. Libra (cardinal air) is action-oriented and compares, weighs ideas and principles. Aquarius (fixed air) is the steadiest and the most stubborn of the air signs.

Air Attributes

The principle of adaptability. Social. Intellectual. Conceptual. The mental plane of human activity. Mind's sensations. Perception. Expression. Abstract Ideas.

Earth

Earth is associated with the winter solstice, the completion of events, and achievements at the end of the cycle. Earth signs are attuned to physical forms and practical ability to utilize and improve the material world.

Taurus, Virgo, and Capricorn are Earth signs. Earth signs are negative, feminine, or receptive signs. Earth signs are a stabilizing influence and refer to the practical and collective affairs of life. Earth is concerned with utilizing and improving the material world. Earth signs are a stabilizing influence.

Earth signs collect and build (most associated with Taurus), are practical and pragmatic (Virgo), and materialistic and cautious (Capricorn). Taurus builds, Virgo labors, and Capricorn manages. Earth signs are grounded in reality. They're also sensual and attached to what they can physically see or touch. Earth signs are skilled at managing and using resources. They want to know what works and to see results for their efforts. Order helps Earth signs feel in control and safe.

Earth Attributes

The principle of stability. Material. Practical. Sense oriented. Dependable. The world of form and substance. The ability to manipulate the environment.

Determining your Elements and Qualities

In this example chart, note how I filled out the table below Chart.

My first teacher assigned a weight fact for the planets. The two luminaries (Sun and Moon) and the Ascendant get three points. The personal planets Mercury, Venus, and Mars get two points. The social planets Jupiter and Saturn get one point while the transpersonal planets (Uranus, Neptune, and Pluto) get a half a point.

The weighting system is related to how we identify the forces the planets express. More on this when we talk about planets.

For example, the Sun is in Capricorn, a cardinal earth sign. Therefore, 3 points are given to both Earth and Cardinal.

	Weight Factor	Sign		Element					Modality/Quality		
				Fire	Earth	Air	Water		Car	Fixed	Mut
Ascendant	3	♈		3					3		
Mid-heaven	2	♑			2				2		
☉	3	♑			3				3		
☽	3	♏					3			3	
☿	2	♒				2				2	
♀	2	♐		2							2
♂	2	♏					2			2	
♃	1	♈		1					1		
♄	1	♍			1						1
♅	0.5	♌		0.5						0.5	
♆	0.5	♏					0.5			0.5	
♇	0.5	♍			0.5						0.5
Total	20.5			6.5	7.5	2	5.5		9	8	3.5

Notice the only planet in an Air sign is Mercury. Not having air doesn't mean you're not smart. It generally means the individual is not very communicative. Slow to form an opinion is not a bad thing.

In this table, there's little mutable. This generally means that the individual doesn't make quick decisions and less adaptable to changing environments. But that not a hard and fast rule because people are different.

The elemental constitution of a chart is one of many chart interpretation techniques. Not all methods apply to every chart.

Homework

Using your chart, fill out the table.

	Weight Factor	Sign		Element					Modality/Quality		
				Fire	Earth	Air	Water		Car	Fixed	Mut
Ascendant	3										
Mid-heaven	2										
☉	3										
☽	3										
☿	2										
♀	2										
♂	2										
♃	1										
♄	1										
♅	0.5										
♆	0.5										
♇	0.5										
Total	20.5										

East and West Hemispheres

There are four hemispheric divisions of the chart - North, South, East, and West. The East Hemisphere contains the tenth to twelfth house and the 1st through the third.

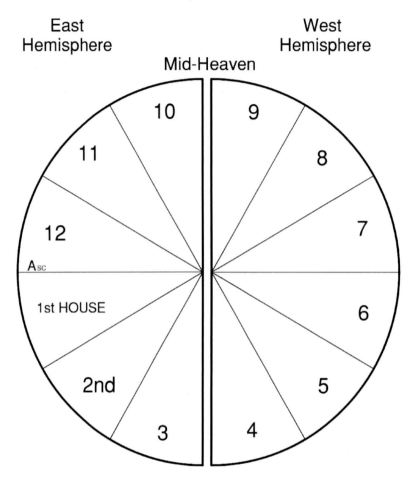

When the majority of planets are found in the east, the natives are self-motivated. They tend to have strong wills and assertive. With more planets in the East, it is an *Independent Chart* and takes on the qualities of Aries (♈).

The West Hemisphere consists of 4th to the 9th Houses or the right half of the chart. Natives with a Western Hemisphere emphasis tend to consider others before making decisions. With most of the planets in the west half, it is a *Dependent Chart* and takes on the qualities of Libra (♎). Planets in the west react and interact with people, ideas, or the public.

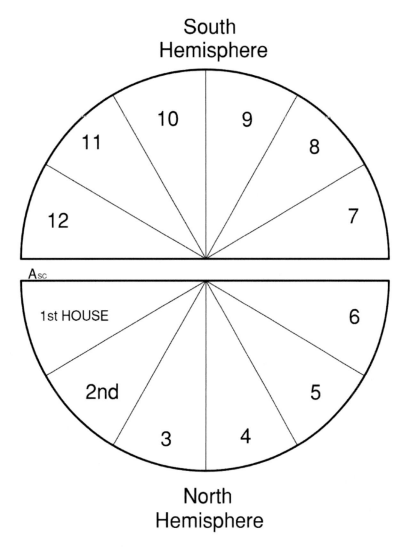

The North Hemisphere includes Houses 1 through 6 and represents *below the Horizon*. Planets in this hemisphere are not visible when you were born. If the Sun is found below, it is called a Night Chart. These houses are considered personal, subjective, and concerned with the development of our character. Natives with most of their planets below the horizon or in the North are more reserved, private and *introverted*. A self-contained person who prefers to keep a low profile.

The South Hemisphere includes Houses 7 through 12 and represents *above the Horizon*. These planets were visible when you were born. Natives with a majority of planets in these houses are more social, objective, and *extroverted*.

The horizon (horizontal division) and meridian (vertical division) create a cross. They are called the four cardinal points or angles.

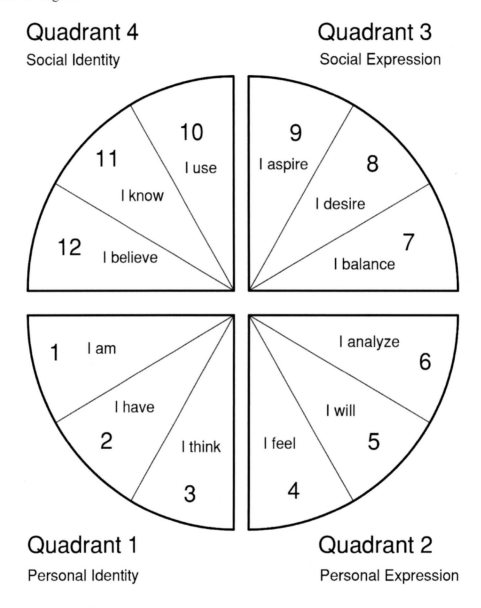

The zodiacal signs and houses are a journey, as expressed in the mottos that are associated with the astrological signs. These mottos will be discussed further in later chapters.

1st Quadrant – Self Development

The first quadrant is concerned with *personal identity* and *awareness of self*. The first three house spends time alone to ask these questions:

1st House. – Who am I?

2nd House – What do I value?

3rd House – What do I think about? What occupies my attention?

Keywords: Self-centered. Independent. Self-development.

2nd Quadrant – Self-expression

The second quadrant is centered on *self-expression* and *creative imagination*. The third through the sixth house is about spending time with family (4th House), children/creative projects (5th House), and coworkers (6th House).

4th – Who is my family?

5th – What do I love?

6th House – How am I useful?

Keywords: Fitting in with friends, co-workers, and integrating with your environment.

3rd Quadrant - Relationships

The third quadrant is concerned with *relationships* and what we learn through others. The seventh through ninth house spends time in relationships (7th House), intimacy (8th House), and high education and religion (9th House).

7th house – How do I relate?

8th House – What do I desire?

9th House – What do I see out there? Awareness of others.

4th Quadrant – Fitting in with society

The fourth quadrant deals with society as a whole – *participation within groups*. The tenth through twelfth Houses spends time in the public (10th House), in organizations that share our values (11th House) and where we retreat to recharge my batteries (12th House).

10th House – Who are the people I can depend on?

11th House – What do I know?

12th House – What do I believe?

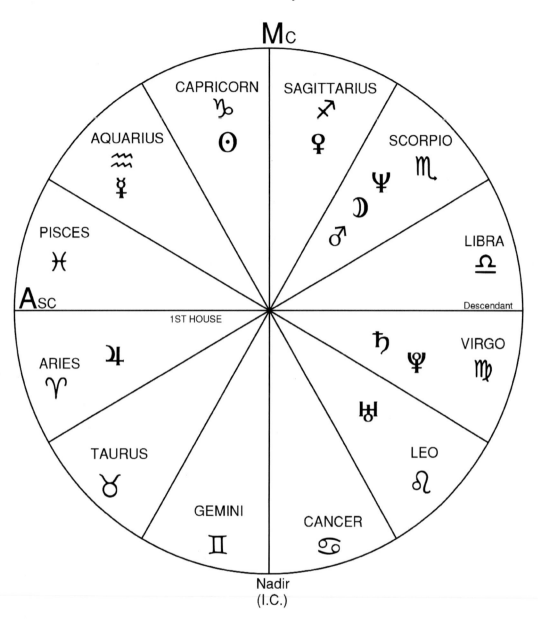

	Weight Factor		Hemisphere				Quadrant
			East Independent	West Dependent	North Introvert	South Extrovert	
☉	3	♑	3			3	4
☽	3	♏		3		3	3
☿	2	♒	2			2	4
♀	2	♐		2		2	3
♂	2	♏		2		2	3
♃	1	♈	1		1		1
♄	1	♍		1	1		2
♅	0.5	♌		0.5	0.5		2
♆	0.5	♏		0.5		0.5	3
♇	0.5	♍		0.5	0.5		2
Total	15.5		6	9.5	3	12.5	

In this chart, the East/West or Independent/Dependent is relatively balanced with the leaning towards the Libra or relating with others.

However, the southern hemisphere has many planets above the horizon. I expect the native with this chart to be an extrovert.

In later chapters, we learn more about how planets are forces that act through the twelve houses. For now, concern yourself with looking at the big picture.

If planets are balanced between left/right or top/bottom, then the individual is relatively balanced.

Homework

Be sure to memorize the symbols of the signs and planets. Review the definitions of four classic elements, Fire, Water, Air, and Earth and the keywords for Cardinal, Fixed, and Mutable.

Using your chart, fill out the table below.

	Weight Factor	Sign	Hemisphere					Quadrant
			East	West	North	South		
☉	3							
☽	3							
☿	2							
♀	2							
♂	2							
♃	1							
♄	1							
♅	0.5							
♆	0.5							
♇	0.5							
Total	20.5							

The shape the planets form in our charts indicates inclinations, character, advantages, and limitations. Not all charts have clear chart shapes. If the chart shape is not apparent, then it's probably not as important as other characteristics of the chart.

See-Saw

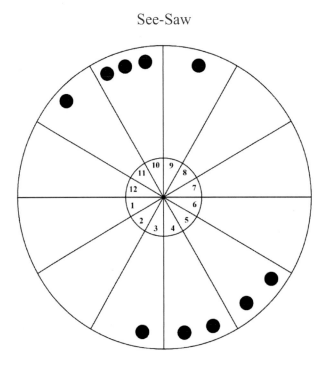

The planets are distributed in two clusters opposite each other, with an empty space of at least 60° on both sides.

Seesaw individuals are striving for balance, which is rarely achieved. Instead, the native goes from one side of the seesaw to the other. Seesaw charts are learning about duality. If the individual doesn't integrate the two halves, they can compete with each other.

The seesaw shape usually has two oppositions that impart a dynamic tension to the native.

The seesaw chart can develop objectivity, deliberation, and knack for conflict resolution.

Seesaw people can seem to live two lives. Their objectivity can make them seem disconnected from their friends and family. Natives seem to choose between opposing values, two careers, or two intimate relationships. Seesaw people feel a need for a romantic relationship to fill the other part that is missing in their lives. .

Bowl Shape

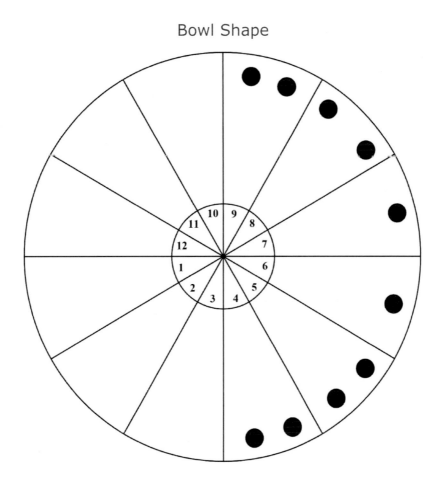

All planets are distributed in one half of the chart at about 180 degrees.

A person with a bowl-shaped chart pattern tends to be focused, self-contained, resourceful, and has strong values. They want meaningful and fulfilling work. They tend to be one-sided and are challenged to integrate the empty half of their chart.

Bowl types with the majority of planets above the horizon are generally extroverted and objective. With the planets below the horizon, the tendency is towards introversion and subjective viewpoint.

Bowls with the planets in the east, or right, of the Midheaven axis, the emphasis is on social outlets. A bowl to the west (left half), the individual is concerned individualistic pursuits.

The first or leading planet in the Bowl (in a clockwise direction) gains in strength. In the chart above, the leading planet is in the fourth house. This planet indicates the energies used to fulfill the native's needs.

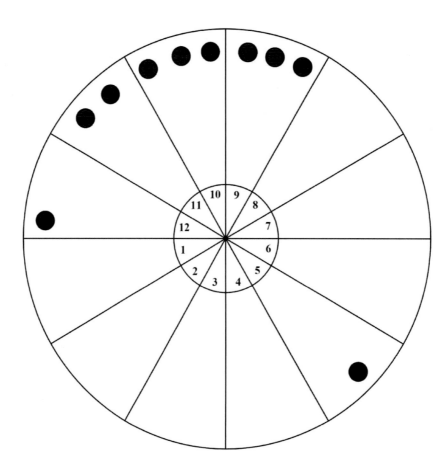

This is similar to the bowl shape, except that one planet opposes the planets that are grouped together. The singleton planet is the handle of the bucket. Its influence is strong and tends to dominate the other planets.

People with bucket-shaped charts are goal orientated – sometimes to extremes. The energies of the bowl planets get focused or funneled into the Singleton. The sign and house position of a Singleton shows how (sign) and in what area of life (house) this effort is directed.

Locomotive Shape

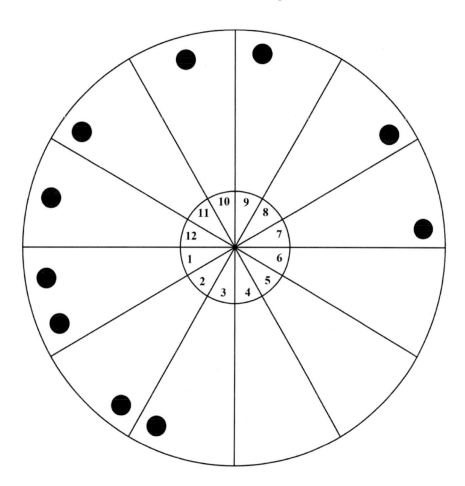

The Locomotive pattern is when all the planets are contained within 240 degrees. Three whole signs or houses are unoccupied.

The planet that rises clockwise following the empty space influences the life of the person with this pattern. In the chart above, the leading planet is in the seventh house. This planet acts as the *locomotive* of the natal chart, driving the individual to achieve goals. They type of purpose is determined by the sign and house of the leading planet.

The empty space in front of the locomotive represents areas in life that are not fully experienced. They feel something is missing. The vacant houses are a sensitive area of the chart that needs attention but is often ignored.

Bundle Shape

(Wedge/Cluster Shape)

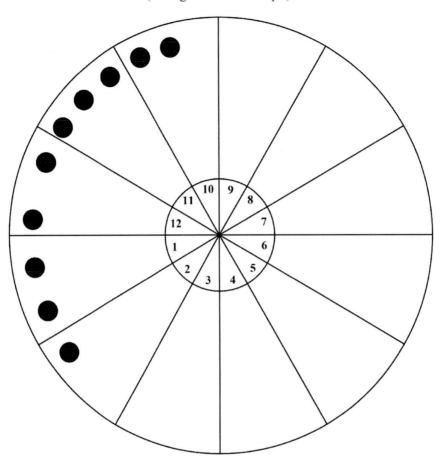

A bundle shape is when the planets span the distance of a trine or four signs of the zodiac.

This chart pattern gives a tenacious and determined mind with a single purpose that is indicated by the signs and houses of the bundle. Natives are self-contained, focused, and resourceful.

With their determined focus, natives tend to lose perspective. They have few interests outside their central focus, which can make them feel isolated.

Splay

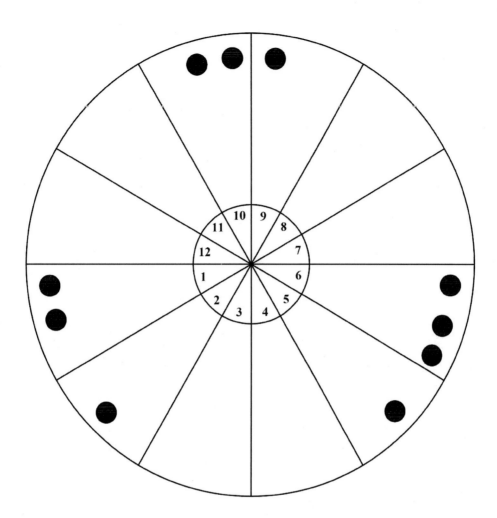

In a splay pattern, the planets spread unevenly around the chart. There is one cluster of two or three planets, with the rest distributed randomly. A grand trine is usually a characteristic of the Splay chart.

People with Splay-shaped charts are individuals with a strong need for freedom. They don't adapt well to the demands or needs of others. Typically, they hold to their views tenaciously and are self-sufficient. They can dislike routine and externally imposed rules and discipline. Like the splash chart below, these people can spread themselves too thin.

Splash Chart

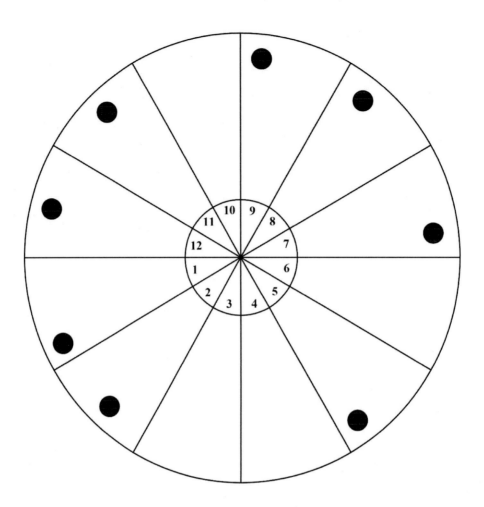

Versatility with many interests

The splash pattern is no pattern at all. The planets are randomly distributed throughout the chart.

These individuals can be confused during youth because they are good at a lot of things and don't know which direction to take.
Individuals with a splash chart are adaptable, versatile, and have many interests and hobbies. They are generally independent people who learn through experience.

Being talented and capable, these natives can scatter their energies and spread themselves too thin.

Sometimes the shape of the chart is hard to find. When in doubt, I consult the tables generated by astrological software. Below is an example from Solar Fire software.

SIGN MODALITIES

Cardinal	♀ ♂ ♄ As		
	Total Points: 4		Weighted Score: 8
Fixed	☽ ☉ ☿ ♅ ♆		
	Total Points: 5		Weighted Score: 10
Mutable	♃ ♇ ☊		
	Total Points: 3		Weighted Score: 2

SIGN ELEMENTS

Fire	♃ ♅		
	Total Points: 2		Weighted Score: 2
Earth	☽ ♀ ♂ ♄ ♇ ☊ As		
	Total Points: 7		Weighted Score: 12
Air	☉ ☿		
	Total Points: 2		Weighted Score: 5
Water	♆		
	Total Points: 1		Weighted Score: 1

HOUSE MODALITIES

Angular	♀ ♂ ♄ ♆		
	Total Points: 4		Weighted Score: 6
Succedent	☽ ☉ ☿ ♅ ♇		
	Total Points: 5		Weighted Score: 10
Cadent	♃ ☊		
	Total Points: 2		Weighted Score: 1

CHART SHAPE
Splash

Chapter 4

Astrological Day and Night – Sect

In astrology, there are many types of days and nights. This is called *sect*. The feminine signs are night, and masculine signs are day. The table below is only one of three different Day/Night arrangements of the signs.

	Sign		Element	Gender	Sect
1	Aries	♈	Fire	Masculine	Day
2	Taurus	♉	Earth	Feminine	Night
3	Gemini	♊	Air	Masculine	Day
4	Cancer	♋	Water	Feminine	Night
5	Leo	♌	Fire	Masculine	Day
6	Virgo	♍	Earth	Feminine	Night
7	Libra	♎	Air	Masculine	Day
8	Scorpio	♏	Water	Feminine	Night
9	Sagittarius	♐	Fire	Masculine	Day
10	Capricorn	♑	Earth	Feminine	Night
11	Aquarius	♒	Air	Masculine	Day
12	Pisces	♓	Water	Feminine	Night

Day and Night Planets

The planets are also assigned a sect.

Night		Both		Day	
☽	Luminary	☿		☉	Luminary
♀	Lesser Fortune			♃	Greater Fortune
♂	Malefic			♄	Malefic

In astrology, there are two luminaries, the Sun and Moon. The Sun rules the day, and the Moon governs the night. The Sun and Moon are *sect lords*. Notice also the two benefices and malefices are assigned one to each sect.

The malefices are the bad guys. Mars stirs things, picks fights, and loves to complain. It is his *raison d etre*. Saturn is Ebenezer Scrooge, a powerful old man that is used to getting his way.

Mars and Saturn tend to be problematic when they are contrary to their sect. That is Saturn in a Night chart and Mars in a Day chart. The malefices act more constructive when there are in their sect. That is Saturn in a Day chart and Mars in a Night chart.

Day and Night Charts

When the Sun is above the horizon, it's called a *day chart*. If the Sun is below the horizon, it's a *night chart*.

Day Chart

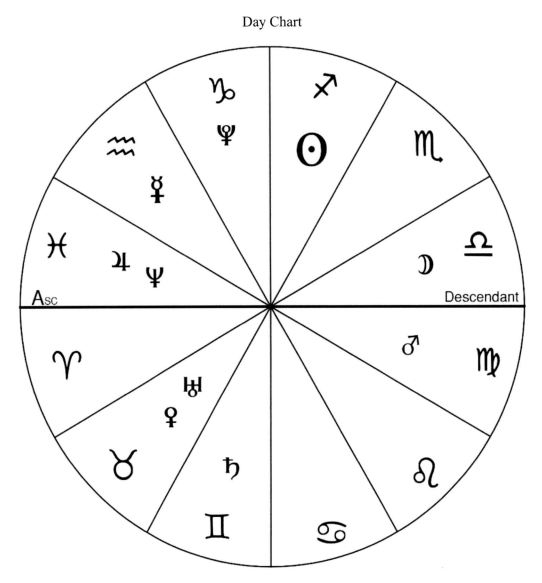

The Sun is above the Ascendant/Descendant and therefore is a Diurnal or Day Chart. In a day chart, the day planets (Sun, Jupiter, and Saturn) have more power and the night planets less. Therefore, the Sun above horizon is an *accidental dignity*.

Night Chart

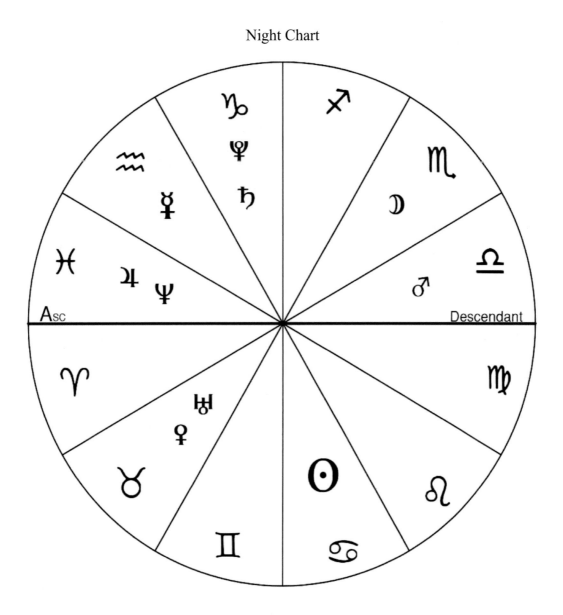

The Sun is below the Ascendant/Descendant and therefore is a Nocturnal or Night Chart. When the Sun is below the horizon, the night planets (Moon, Venus, and Mars) have more power and push their agendas, while the day planets take a back seat.

Hayz

Hayz is an accidental dignity that occurs when a masculine or diurnal planet is above the horizon in a male sign; or a feminine, nocturnal planet below the horizon in a female sign by night.

The feminine or night planets are the Moon and Venus. The masculine or day planets are the Sun, Jupiter, and Saturn. Mars is a male and a night planet.

Hayz of Day Planets in a Day Chart						
	Planets above the Horizon in either of these signs					
☉ ♃ ♄	♈	♊	♌	♎	♐	♒

Hayz of Night Planets in a Night Chart						
	Planets above the Horizon in either of these signs					
☽ ♀	♉	♋	♍	♏	♑	♓

For example, Moon in Taurus in a Night Chart and it's above the horizon is in its Hayz.

Hayz of Mars - Night Planet in a Night Chart						
	Mars above the Horizon in either of these signs					
♂	♈	♊	♌	♎	♐	♒

Mars is a masculine planet but is Hayz in a Night Chart when above the horizon. By day, Mars is aggressive and causes problems. However, by night he takes on more protective and defensive energy. He helps sustain activity to finish projects.

Chart Interpretation Technique

One technique to evaluate your chart is to examine the strength of a chart is to examine *sect lord* and their companions. The Sun rules the day, and his companions are Jupiter and Saturn. The Moon governs the night, and her companions are Mars and Venus.

In the later chapter on Accidental Dignities, the figure below is explained.

Planets in angular houses (1st, 4th, 7th, and 10th) are powerful. Succedent house are good while cadent houses 3rd, 6th, 9th, and 12th) are weak.

Generally, in a day chart, if the day planets (Sun, Jupiter, and Mars) are in angular houses, they have the environment necessary to carry out their plan. Also, in a Night Chart, night planets (Moon, Venus, and Mars) have a favorable atmosphere in the angular houses.

Summary

Jupiter is slightly more benefic in a Day Chart, and Venus is slightly more benefic in a Night Chart.

Saturn acts more constructively in a Day Chart and Mars in a Night Chart.

In general, Day means extrovert and objective. Night means introvert, subjective, and introspective.

Homework

Determine if you have a Day Chart or Night Chart and fill out the appropriate table.

Mercury does not receive the dignity of Hayz and is omitted from the exercise.

D = Day and means masculine signs (Aries, Gemini, Leo, Libra, Sagittarius, and Aquarius).

N = Night and means negative signs (Taurus, Cancer, Virgo, Scorpio, Capricorn, and Pisces).

M = Masculine Sign

F = Feminine Sign

Day Chart Example

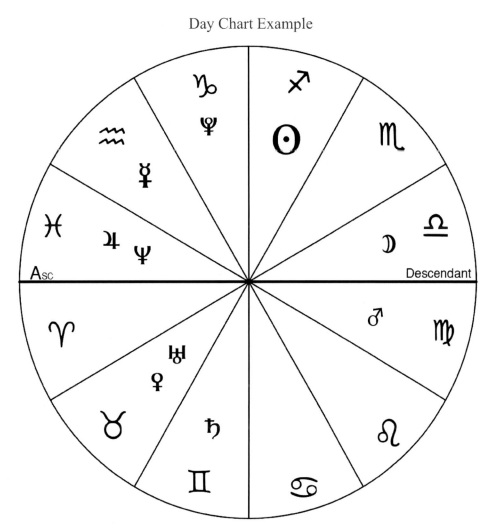

Day Chart					
Planet		Above/Below the Horizon	Sign	Polarity	Dignity	House
Sun	☉	Above	♐	M	Hayz	9
Jupiter	♃	Above	♓	F	None	12
Saturn	♄	Below	♊	M	None	3

The Sun is a masculine planet above the horizon in a masculine sign. The Sun is in its Hayz.

Jupiter is masculine, above the horizon, but is **not** in a male sign.

Saturn is a male planet in a masculine sign; however, he is **below** the horizon.

Night Chart Example

Night Chart						
Planet		Above/Below the Horizon	Sign	Polarity	Dignity	House
Moon	☽	Above	♏	N	Hayz	8
Venus	♀	Below	♉	N	None	2
Mars	♂	Above	♎	D	Hayz	7

The Moon and Scorpio are feminine. The Moon is above the horizon and can be seen in the night sky. The Moon is Hayz.

Venus and Taurus are feminine. Venus is below the horizon and in the same hemisphere as the Sun. Therefore, Venus is not in Hayz.

Mars and Libra are masculine. In the chart above, he is above the horizon and shines in the night sky. Generally, Mars behaves better by night because he's introspective before taking action.

Homework

Depending on your chart, fill out the appropriate table.

Day Chart						
Planet		Above/Below the Horizon	Sign	Polarity	Dignity	House
Sun	☉					
Jupiter	♃					
Saturn	♄					

Night Chart						
Planet		Above/Below the Horizon	Sign	Polarity	Dignity	House
Moon	☽					
Venus	♀					
Mars	♂					

Additional Homework

There are also two additional sect related dignities or conditions. They are minor considerations.

However, when a planet has no dignity, it is considered *Peregrine*. This is a disability that modern astrologers assign a value of negative five. Many astrologers don't use sect and miss this minor dignity that can change a planet's score from -5 to +1.

In its own Light

Day planets prefer to be above the horizon during the day and below by night. Night planets prefer to be below the horizon by day and above the horizon by night. This is called *in its own light*.

In its own Similitude

When masculine planets are in male signs and feminine planets are in female signs, it is called, *in its own similitude*.

Chapter 5

An Overview of the Zodiacal Signs

The mottos for the zodiacal signs are,

Signs		Motto	Motto		Signs
Aries	♈	I am	I relate	♎	Libra
Taurus	♉	I have	I desire	♏	Scorpio
Gemini	♊	I think	I perceive I aspire	♐	Sagittarius
Cancer	♋	I feel	I use I make use of	♑	Capricorn
Leo	♌	I will. I am special	I know	♒	Aquarius
Virgo	♍	I analyze I discriminate	I believe	♓	Pisces

Aries is the opposite sign of Libra. From one perspective, Aries and Libra are the same energy but expressed differently. The underlying question of Aries/Libra is, Who am I?

Aries is a cardinal fire sign ruled by Mars. He is the explorer that goes it alone. Venus rules Libra an Air sign. She discovers her identity by relating to other people — the self (Aries) and not-self (Libra).

Taurus and Scorpio are fixed signs. Taurus is fixed earth ruled by Venus, who is focused on values and things. Mars rules Scorpio, a fixed water sign. His concern is with emotional security and stability.

Gemini and Sagittarius are aspects of mind. Gemini, ruled by Mercury, looks carefully at the details. Jupiter rules Sagittarius and is focused on the big picture.

Cancer and Capricorn are cardinal signs that initiate action. The Moon rules Cancer, and she's concerned about feelings. Saturn rules Capricorn, and emotions are irrelevant. He would rather be respected than liked.

Leo and Aquarius are fixed signs. Leo is fixed fire ruled by the Sun. As king, he's the lead singer. Aquarius is a fixed air ruled by Saturn. He is content being a voice in a choir.

Virgo and Pisces are mutable signs. Virgo is mutable earth where Mercury is in Rulership and Exaltation. In an Earth sign, Mercury's interest is in the material and practical. For Virgo, seeing is believing. Pisces is a Water sign ruled by Jupiter. His faith is overflowing in watery Pisces.

Homework

Combine the two concepts (Element and Modality) and write a short phrase that describes the signs.

Element	Symbol	Attributes
Fire	△	Spontaneous, reactive, impulsive, fearless, courageous, assertive. Identity issues.
Water	▽	Fluid, emotional, intuitive. Emotional issues.
Air	△ (with line)	Intellectual, detached, communicative, social. Social and intellectual issues.
Earth	▽ (with line)	Practical, pragmatic, cautious, sensual. Practical issues.

Modality	Attributes
Cardinal	Initiates action
Fixed	Security. Stability. Intensity.
Mutable	Adaptable. Changeable. Assimilation & Transmission

Example:

Aries: Cardinal Fire: Initiates action (cardinal) to develop identity (Fire).

Taurus: Fixed Earth:

Gemini: Mutable Air:

Cancer: Cardinal Water:

Leo: Fixed Fire:

Virgo: Mutable Earth:

Libra: Cardinal Air:

Scorpio: Fixed Water:

Sagittarius: Mutable Fire:

Capricorn: Cardinal Earth:

Aquarius: Fixed Air:

Pisces: Mutable Water:

Chapter 6

The Astrological Signs

Aries – ♈

Modality	Cardinal		Ruler	♂
Element	Fire		Exaltation	☉
Anatomy	Head, face, brain		I am	

Aries is the explorer, pioneer, and warrior archetype. With Mars in rulership, he tends to be impatient and combative. Aries natives like to lead and plan; they dislike taking orders. It is best to explain to Aries the reason why a particular goal is advantageous, and they'll take it upon their initiative.

The Sun's is Exaltation in Aries. In his Leo rulership, the Sun does not like to leave his lair. Aries is a cardinal sign that initiates action. Here the Sun works outside his comfort zone and is enriched with new experiences and skills.

Arian individuals do best in work where they will be free to express their ideas and put them into execution, and where they can direct the activities of other people. As children, they dislike restrictions.

Aries Attributes

Like all cardinal signs, Aries is good at starting things but not so good at finishing.

+   Assertive/Active/Initiating. Leadership. Outgoing. Adventurous. Courageous. Confident. Expressive. Independent. Ambitious. Enthusiastic. Enjoys a good time (Fire signs in general). Pioneering. Leader. Independent. Taking charge.

-      Selfish. Impulsive. Rude. Foolhardy. Egotistical. Combative/Competitive. Pushy. Sarcastic. Dictatorial. Reckless. Dominating. Abusive. Destructive. Excessive Risk-taking. Bad temper, but anger is short-lived.

Taurus – ♉

Modality	Fixed	Ruler	♀
Element	Earth	Exaltation	☽
Anatomy	Neck, throat, larynx, jaw, ears	I have	

The Taurus archetype is the musician, gardener, and lover of nature. It is the only sign where the two female planets, The Moon (Exaltation) and Venus (Rulership), are both dignified. Natives are generally kind, friendly and affectionate disposition, but can be fixed in their ways and opinions.

Taurus natives are determined, practical, and dutiful. The fixed nature of the sign gives them thoroughness. Once they start a course of action, they persist despite obstacles and opposition.

Ordinarily, they are good-natured and love comfort. They hate to give offense and are slow to take it. They dislike arguments, but when their convictions are attacked, they will defend them determinedly.

The Moon is exalted in Taurus. In a Fixed Earth sign, the Moon is emotionally stable, which makes it easier for natives to tap into their intuition.

Taurus Attributes

Slow and persistent. Establishing self-reliance through constant and steady efforts. Enjoys the physical environment. Materialistic. Sense oriented. Motivated by material insecurity. Possessive and practical. Inertia and determination.

+   Practical. Steadfast/Persevering/Patient. Cautious. Pragmatic. Reliable. Stable. Loyal (Fixed signs in general). Sensual. Natural. Determined. Affectionate. Resourceful. Strong.

-      Possessive (Fixed signs in general). Jealous. Slow to change. Stubborn. Indulgent. Hedonistic. Materialistic. Greedy/Stingy. Lazy. Dogmatic. Controlling. Inflexible.

Gemini – ♊

Modality	Mutable	Ruler	☿
Element	Air	Exaltation	N.N.
Anatomy	Hands & Arms. Lungs. Nervous system	I think	

N.N. = North Node.

The Gemini archetype is the storyteller, messenger, trickster, and eternal youth. They learn quickly and usually have good memories. However, they can be lax about verifying what they have heard or read.

Gemini natives like changes of scene and like work that enables them to move about, make new acquaintances, and a variety of experiences. Routine bores Gemini.

Gemini is adaptable. Adaptability, if overemphasized, can express as an inability to concentrate enough to accomplish anything. We must be able to adapt, but too much changeability can frustrate our accomplishments.

The North Node is exalted in Gemini. The North Node is the point where the Moon crosses from Earth's southern hemisphere to the North. More on the Moon's nodes in later chapters.

Gemini Attributes

The concrete mind. Changeability. Duality. Restlessness. Literary and academic matters. Diversification. Ambiguous and curious. Continually interacting to gather information. Perception and verbalization of connections. Learning and teaching about social and intellectual ideas.

+   Curious. Perceptive. Mental. Knowledgeable. Communicative. Neutral. Adaptable. Versatile. Inquisitive. Social. Spontaneous. Versatile. Friendly. Lively. Witty. Comical. Youthful.

-    Restless. Nervous. Unreliable. Uncommitted. Fickle. Ungrateful. Scattered. Superficial. Immature. Selfish. Mischievous. Overly Talkative. Lacking follow through.

Cancer – ♋

Modality	Cardinal	Ruler	☽
Element	Water	Exaltation	♃
Anatomy	Breast, stomach	I feel	

Cancer is ruled by the Moon and is the Mother archetype and home lover. Their sense of family solidarity is strong, sometimes to the point of clannishness. They are happiest amid accustomed surroundings. Often, they are patriotic, and this is an extension of their love of home.

Cancer people hate pain and dislike controversy. Natives avoid physical danger. Although they have less physical courage than found in Fire signs, they often make up for it with moral courage.

Their sensitive natures incline them to be retiring and quiet. At the same time, they frequently found in positions of public trust.

With the Moon, the ruler of Cancer, natives are usually fond of change and adapt themselves quickly to new conditions.

Cancer is impressionable. Many psychics have strong Cancer or Pisces aspects in their chart. Scorpio, being a fixed sign, is more occult than psychic.

Cancer Attributes

The home and family. Receptivity. Sensitivity and feelings. Maternal instincts. Action and initiative applied to emotional and soul concerns. Emotionally engaged. Tenacious with feelings. Protective of whatever it identifies with emotionally.

+ Empathic. Gentle. Nurturing. Protective. Supportive. Sensitive. Traditional. Domestic. Imaginative. Intuitive. Comfort-Oriented. Tenacious. Family oriented. Mystical. Creative. Contemplative.

- Clingy. Moody. Defensive. Needy. Guilt/manipulative. A need to be needed. Crabby. Worried. Attached to the past. Irritable. Dependent. Insecure. Clannish. Snobby. Fearful. Shy. Indulgent. Hysterical. Manipulative. Lazy. Feeling sorry for yourself.

Leo – ♌

Modality	Fixed	Ruler	☉
Element	Fire	Exaltation	None
Anatomy	Heart, spine	I will	

Leo is the ruler (king or queen), performer, protector archetype. Commanding and magnanimous, Leos like to rule. It is different from Aries need to lead. Leo people are willing to stay in the background as long as they have authority.

Leo is a fixed sign that is stable and persistent as it progresses towards its goal. They have strong powers of concentration. They are intense and persevering about whatever they think or feel.

This fixed quality gives lasting and strong likes and dislikes. The fiery nature of Leo imparts a quick temper. Like all fire signs, they seldom hold a grudge. And if their temper has flared from a misunderstanding, they are quick to make amends. What angers a Leo is anything petty or cowardly. They hate deceit.

Leos spread joy and good spirits wherever they go. They tend to warm up any place they enter.

Leo natives are cooperative if properly approached. Leo enjoys helping people in need – magnanimous. Friendships with Leos are usually rewarding because of their loyal and affectionate nature.

Leo Attributes

Finds security and stability through creative activities. The search for secure and stable identity. Giving generously to an appreciative audience.

+   Active. **Charismatic. Noble.** Generous. Creative. Loving. Enthusiastic. Dramatic. Expressive. Affectionate. Honorable. Courageous. Self-confident. **Playful and fun-loving (fire signs). Romantic. Respectful.** Magnanimous. Hospitable. Caring. Open.

-     Showy. Arrogant. **Egotistical. Narcissistic.** Flamboyant. Selfish. Childish. Dictatorial. Prideful. Protective of vanity. **Stubborn.** An unwarranted need for praise – Narcissistic.

Virgo – ♍

Modality	Mutable	Ruler	☿
Element	Earth	Exaltation	☿
Anatomy	Small Intestines	I analyze	

Virgo is the craftsman, servant, and master archetypes. Virgo is correlated with the natural sixth house of service.

Virgo is concerned with self-improvement and issues of health. Because illness allows us to stop routine activities and focus on health. Illness gives time for reflection and introspection.

The Mercury rulership gives Virgos quick tempers but are seldom combative. They prefer reason to force. Virgos either have a closet filled with clothes or minimalist.

The Virgo types are industrious. They love order, and their homes are usually spotless, or its polarity, sloppy. Generally speaking, neat Virgos have some parts of their life that chaotic, usually a closet. The untidy Virgos are fond of organized piles.

Virgos are good at handling details; they learn quickly, and like Gemini, they have good hand and eye coordination. Virgos usually like to be around people at work and a hermit at home. Virgos need periods of isolation and silence more than any other sign.

In Virgo, Mercury is both *Exalted* and in *Rulership*. The Virgo mind has an acute perception of the subtle details that others miss. Their highly developed mind tends to be critical and judgmental of others.

Virgo Attributes

Service and Health. Discriminating. Selective processing. Prudent and judicious. Rearranging, refining, and perfecting itself to remain useful. Spontaneous (mutable signs in general). Helpful. Humble. A need to serve. Discriminating and sorting the useful from the non-useful. Detail-oriented. Studious.

+   Dependable. Helpful. Conscientious. Honest. Efficient. **Analytical.** Modest. Intelligent. Thoughtful. Willing to allow others in the limelight. Ready to admit when wrong. Organized. Thorough. **Service-Oriented. Hard-working. Industrious.** Reserved.

-    Critical of others and self. Skeptical. Prudish. **Nit Picky.** Fastidious. Worrisome. Nervous quality. Matter of fact. Repressed. Perfectionist. Timid.

Libra – ♎

Modality	Cardinal	Ruler	♀
Element	Air	Exaltation	♄
Anatomy	Kidneys. Lower back.	I relate I balance	

Venus rules Libra. She is the artist, diplomat, and lawmaker archetype.

Librans can be impractical because they are learning about balance, which requires being unbalanced to compare it to being balanced. Libra experiences the highs and depths of emotion, more than other signs except for Capricorn. With Saturn rulership, Capricorn experiences the depths, but not the heights.

If things are too balanced, Libra likes to stir of the pot so they can play peacemaker.

Librans love peace and harmony. Dissension tears them apart. They cannot bear conflict, so they appease. They are sometimes are too agreeable for the sake of avoiding friction.

However, if their sense of justice affronted or their motives questioned, you will see their anger.

Librans love beauty, and they usually dress well because their appearance is important to them. Charming settings feed their souls.

Libra Attributes

Emotional. Temperamental. Artistic. Just. Cooperative. Equalizing tendencies. Adaptive and graceful. Harmonizing relations to encourage affinity and balance. Completion through relationship. Initiates action on social and conceptual levels.

+   Diplomatic. Graceful. Refined. Beauty. Peaceful. Fair. Strong principals. Artistic. Polite. Affectionate. Persuasive. Lawful.

-       Superficial. Impractical. Phony. Vain. Flirtatious. Indecisive. The imposition of principals and tyranny of ideals. Procrastinating. Approval-Seeking. Passive-Aggressive. Deceitful.

Scorpio – ♏

Modality	Fixed		Ruler	♂, ♆
Element	Water		Exaltation	♅
Anatomy	Genitals. Bladder. Bowels		I desire	

Scorpio is the night house of Mars. Night suggest secrets and the unknown. Therefore the Scorpio archetype is the investigator, researcher, therapist, and transformer. Scorpio keeps secrets.

Scorpios have complex personalities and are the most intense sign in the zodiac. This intensity and penetrating nature can be expressed as compassion or cruelty, especially mental cruelty.

All the water signs have a mystical quality. As a fixed sign, the psychic qualities of Scorpio are more controlled.

The fixed nature of Scorpio can focus on projects. They are tireless workers (Mars rulership) with executive ability and constructive power.

As a water sign, Scorpios bonds to others by sharing emotions. Through strong emotions, positive or negative, Scorpio connects.

Although their penetrating nature may be overwhelming at times, Scorpios are loyal friends (fixed signs in general).

Scorpio Attributes

Private. A Search for emotional and soul security. Penetration through intense emotional power. Search for truth. Confrontational. Intense and resourceful. Catalyzing change to provoke greater emotional honesty and growth. See things as black and white. Sex. Will. Life and death issues. Magic and occultism. Regeneration.

+ Integrity. Intensity. Focused. **Magnetic. Resourceful.** Loyal. Passionate. **Mysterious.** Sexual. Persevering. Secretive. Depth. Transformation. The ability to undergo great change. Healing self and others. Spiritual and truthful. **Probing.** Perceptive. Wants to penetrate the surface to find out what things are made of.

   Extreme. Vengeful. Suspicious. Domineering. Controlling. **Obsessive. Possessive.** Jealous. Seductive. Moody. Emotionally complicated. **Emotional and mental cruelty.**

Sagittarius – ♐

Modality	Mutable	Ruler	♃
Element	Fire	Exaltation	South Node
Anatomy	Hips. Thighs. Muscles. Liver.	I perceive I understand	

Sagittarius is the explorer, inspirational, and scholarly archetype.

Sagittarius loves freedom and hates routine. Like all fire signs, they like a good time, make friends easily, and have a quick temper. Sagittarius is sometimes called fickle because of their need for freedom and change.

Jupiter, the planet of faith, rules Sagittarius. Their optimism is infectious. However, their confidence in other people are sometimes not well-founded, and this can lead to trouble.

Like its polar opposite sign Gemini, Sagittarius loves to learn. They enjoy outdoor activities, sports, traveling, and dancing. They usually have a fondness for horses and dogs.

With Jupiter's rulership, Sagittarius is generous and charitable. They hate double-dealing and concealment and are frank and open in their speech.

Sagittarius Attributes

Aspiring. Frank. Philosophical. Religion. Inspiration. Idealism. Academic matters and sports. Spacious. Willing to believe in new ideas. A desire to know.

+   Idealistic. Spontaneous. **Honest**. Extroverted. Exploration. Adventurous. Expansive. Generous. Cheerful. Optimistic. **Confident**. Blessed with the luck that comes from their attitude. **Outdoorsy**. **Humorous**. Scholarly. **Philosophical**. Independent.

-      Hypocritical Exaggerators. Careless. Irresponsible. Indulgent. **Dogmatic**. Judgmental. Restless. It looks at the big picture without consideration of the details. Opinionated. **Uncommitted**. **Foolish**. Self-deceived. **Cruelly blunt**. **Over-conventional**.

Capricorn – ♑

Modality	Cardinal		Ruler	♄
Element	Earth		Exaltation	♂
Anatomy	Knees. Bones. Skin. Teeth. Hair.		I use	

Capricorn archetype is the ambitious business person, executive, wise elder. They make practical leaders that create material success and gain. For thousands of years, envy has masqueraded as a virtue. It is a lie that to be spiritual that we must renounce the good things of the physical plane.

Cardinal signs like Capricorn, tend towards executive pursuits because they initiate action. As an earth sign, Capricorn expresses itself constructively. They are cautious and frugal and make the most of their means and opportunities.

Capricorn is ambitious and recognizes their talents and weakness. They measure their powers and use them to bring about their desired goal. They are not easily discouraged. Persistent, patient, concentrated effort enables them to succeed in the long run.

Capricorn people are thoughtful, serious, and conservative. Capricorn dislikes being patronized or criticized. If you lower their stature, they can be vindictive. Capricorn is quick to judge the motives of others and fails to realize that most everybody acts from mixed motives.

Capricorn is practical, economical, and can be meticulousness in dress and manner. They share with Virgo an awareness of details. Capricorn is concerned with customs and appearances.

Capricorns do not change their opinions easily and are inclined to a materialistic interpretation of life. Therefore, they make better occultists or scientist than mystics. They are seldom emotional about the results of their investigations. Once a Capricorn recognizes the need for adjustment, they change faster than the mutable signs because of the perseverance of Saturn.

Capricorn Attributes

Diplomatic. Conservative. Initiates activity in the material world. Status. Politics. Law. Reliance on social structures. Stability and the father. Self-organizing. Sober and dignified. Establishing integrity. Works to attain mastery. Impersonal determination to get things done.

+   Good at planning and organizing. Structured. Efficient. Ambitious and seeming selfish, but when attains goals gives freely. Hard-working. Cautious. Practical. Responsible. Disciplined. Paternal. Tenacious. Conservative. Resourceful. Wise. Professional. Hardworking. Enterprising.

-   Fearful. Selfish. Insensitive. Pessimistic. Rigid. Controlling. Stern. Cynical. Demanding. Bossy. Cold. Ruthless. Insensitive. Worrying. The ends justify the means.

Aquarius – ♒

Modality	Fixed	Ruler	♄, ♅
Element	Air	Exaltation	None
Anatomy	Ankles. Shins. Calves.	I know	

The Aquarius archetype is the genius, humanitarian, inventor, scientist, truth-seeker, and astrologer. They are thoughtful people. The Aquarian temperament needs its individuality. Because of their desire to be different, they can appear eccentric or foolish.

Aquarians are intensely aware of their inner life. Urania is one of the nine Muses in Greek Mythology and is attributed to astrology and universal love. Aquarians like to improvise and invent. They tend towards scientific, occult, metaphysical, and astrological studies.

Aquarius desires to get at the facts, to uncover the truth of things. Things of the mind are real to them. As one of the fixed signs, Aquarius has perseverance. They can get so involved in their thoughts and projects that they become inaccessible to the rest of the world. The absent-minded professor archetype can be found with planets in Aquarius or the 11th house.

Aquarius enjoys discussions and debates without getting emotionally involved. As an Air sign, Aquarius is the least fixed. They can accept new data and suddenly switch their opinions based on new facts. Aquarius can be tactless, which is distressing to emotionally sensitive types. Out of curiosity, Aquarius can ask embarrassingly direct questions.

Aquarians usually don't display intense emotions. Their type of love is an all-encompassing, rather than a deep personal attachment. If your looking for an individual to fulfill your emotional security, an Aquarian is not for you. If you want your freedom and individuality respected, date an Aquarius.

Aquarius Attributes

Detached focus. Inventive. An unpredictable style of interacting to sustain its social freedom. Detached coordination of people and concepts. Little sense of individual self. Often defined themselves by the group they associate with. A tendency to think about others. Science. Music. Genius. Political movements and revolutions. Humanitarianism, group, and collective ideals.

+   **Friendly. Interesting.** Independent. **Unconventional.** Original. Fair. Intellectual. Inventive. Innovative. True individuals. Value their right to be their person. Not followers. Humanitarian. **Tolerant.** Rebel/Reformer.

-       **Aloof.** Impersonal. Uncomfortable with emotion. **Weird.** Eccentric. **Shocking.** Contrary. Reactionary. **Unpredictable.** Rebel/Reformer. Unreliable. Impractical. Lost in Ideas. Stubborn (fixed signs in general).

Pisces – ♓

Modality	Mutable	Ruler	♃, ♆
Element	Water	Exaltation	Venus
Anatomy	Feet	I believe	

Venus, creative imagination, is exalted in Pisces. Therefore the Pisces archetype is the mystic, poet, dreamer, musician, psychic, and visionary artist. In water signs, the Moon is dignified by mixed triplicity. Water signs are natural psychics, Pisceans feel the invisible side of life. They respond emotionally (the Moon) and devotionally (Jupiter) to the influence of the forces behind the veil of appearances. In spiritual practices, Pisces prefers the devotional path.

Pisceans often express telepathic rapport with others and are not always aware of it. They can be receiving others' thoughts and emotions and think that they are their own.

Pisceans can be methodical, doing things accurately and completely. These traits, combined with their creative imagination, make good artists. Creative imagination negatively expressed, Pisces can be dreamers and escapists. Afflictions involving the Moon and Jupiter can give Pisceans many frustrations and sorrows. Pisces can suffer from depression.

Pisces Attributes

Absorbing. Dissolving differences and boundaries to realize all-encompassing unity. Healing compassion for all that suffer. Lives in the feeling world more than any other sign. Personal identity issues. Chameleon. Gives indiscriminately. Has difficulty drawing limits. Impressionable. Mystical. Psychic. Attuned to the non-tangible.

+   Imaginative. Visionary. Spiritual. Intuitive. Idealistic. Vulnerable. Empathic. Tender. Compassionate. Sympathetic. Loving. Benevolent. Giving. Responsive. Caring. Open. Devoted. Artistic. Poetic. Meditative. Gentle. Mystical. Romantic. Sacrificial. Perceptive.

-    Vague. Unfocused. Deceitful. **Delusional.** Escapist. **Alcoholism and addiction.** Victim. Martyr. Savior/Saint. Disorganized. Fanaticism. Sacrificial. **Depressed. Abused. Passive.** Evasive. **Indiscriminate.**

Like the astrological signs, there are twelve houses in astrology. However, do not confuse the Houses wheel with the Zodiac wheel. They are two different wheels that will be explained in the chapter on the ascendant or rising sign.

The houses represent the physical surroundings of our different experiences. Consider the analogy of a play. The planets are the actors. The signs are the roles they play. The houses are the settings — for example, Mars in Cancer in the 10th House. Mars, the warrior, is wearing the apron strings of a Mother in the house that represents our public image and status. This could be a man or woman at work (10th House) who is a nurturing and protective (Cancer) towards their employees. He/she may take an active interest in the personal lives of employees and defend them as their children.

There are several good astrology texts and online sources that tabulates the plants in all signs and houses. I recommended *The Only Way to Learn Astrology,* but there are other good books. Read what they say about your planets in houses. Then read all the planets in all the signs. Understanding the big picture will help you understand your chart.

Layout

The houses are numbered counterclockwise around a chart. The dividing point between the ending of one house and the start of a new house is called a *Cusp*.

The most important houses are the 1st, 4th, 7th, and 10th houses. These are called the *angular houses* because their cusps coincide with the four angles:

1st House Cusp – Ascendant or Rising Sign.

4th House Cusp – I.C. or Nadir

7th House Cusp – Descendant

10th House Cusp – M.C. or Mid-heaven

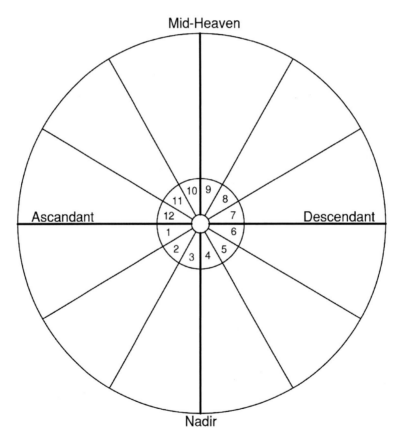

Planets locate in the 1st, 4th, 7th, or 10th house are accidentally dignified, especially if they are located within 4 degrees the house cusp. Accidentally dignified planets are more powerful. This is especially true for the Sun and Moon.

Each zodiac sign is naturally associated with a House. It has a house that most corresponds to its archetype or Natural Ruler. The natural houses of the planets and signs are shown below.

Astrological signs are classified by modality (Cardinal, Fixed, and Mutable). Houses are organized by their mode of expression, Angular, Succedent, and Cadent.

House		Expression
Angular	1, 4, 7 & 10	Action
Succedent	2, 5, 8, & 11	Security
Cadent	3, 6, 9, 12	Change & Adaptation

Angular houses represent action and relate to cardinal signs (Aries, Cancer, Libra, and Capricorn). Succedent houses represent the purpose and represent stabilization and refer to the Fixed signs (Taurus, Leo, Scorpio, and Aquarius). Cadent houses are represented by transition, change, and adaptation and are related to the mutable signs (Gemini, Virgo, Sagittarius, and Pisces).

Elemental Triplicity

Also, the houses are classified by their elements.

Triplicity	Houses	Keyword
Fire	1, 3, & 9	Identity
Earth	2, 6, & 10	Material
Air	3, 7, & 11	Social, Intellect
Water	4, 8, & 12	Soul, Emotions

1st – House of Self

The first house represents your personality and physical appearance. It also describes your awareness of self and early childhood experiences that leave a deep impression on the forming individual.

The cusp of the first is called the *Ascendant* or *Rising Sign*. Planets conjunct the first house cusp will be *embodied* and *acted* out by the personality.

Attributes

New enterprises and beginnings. Resourcefulness. Personal identity. The awareness of self. Self-image. What I show you. Physical appearance. What seeks personification. What activates your energy. The personality. The conditions of birth. Overall attitude (persona). Behavior. Traits and characteristics. Outlook and impressions. Ego.

2nd – House of Values

The second house refers to possessions and financial affairs. It also symbolizes material and immaterial things that you value, including your self-worth. The second house and the planets that occupy the house indicate your talents and resources.

Attributes

Money. Belongings, property, acquisitions. Self-worth. Security or how security is defined. Earned income.

Resources. Talents. Material possessions. Attachment. Values. Security in a material world. A skill that provides you with your material needs. Possessions and one's attitude toward possessions. Inherent qualities.

3rd – House of Communication

The third house experiences test our ability to think, how to make conscious and intelligent decisions to the challenges of our environment.

It symbols brothers and sisters and all forms of communication.

Attributes

Early education and childhood environment. Siblings and neighbors.

Local travel and transportation. Short journeys.

Communication. Intelligence. Thinking, speaking, and writing styles. The concrete mind. What needs communication. How experience is converted into information. Concepts and language. How we gather information. Expressing yourself in the culture. Learning rules. Writings.

4th – House of Home and Family

The fourth house experiences deal with home, family, and traditions. Fourth house experiences test our stability and personal space. It is where our needs for privacy and our lifestyle to find satisfaction. The fourth house is where we clan together and form tribes.

Attributes

Your security. The home and conditions of home life. Family. Feelings. How we nurture ourselves. Privacy needs. Clan/tribal instincts. Inner security. Mother or mother figures.

Real estate matters. Ancestry. Heritage. Roots. Comfort. End of matters. End of life. Fame after death.

5th – House of Pleasure and Play

The fifth house shows your emotional attitude and how you express affection. It also symbolizes how you have fun and play. Fifth house experiences involve the acts of *creating*, including children.

Attributes

Children. Pleasure. Fun and games. Entertainment. Speculation/gambling. Amusement. Creativity. Casual relationships. The magical child. Creative and destructive powers. What needs love to come alive. Talent. Artistic style. Creative self-expression. Love affairs as amusement. Romance.

6th – House of Health and Service

The sixth house refers to how we deal with our inadequacies and how we improve ourselves through introspection. It is the house of work and health.

The sixth house issues are concerned with a *personal crisis* and the way to meet them, including illness. Illness requires us to adjust our attitude and physical activities. Thus the sixth house refers to all experiences of healing and the fear of sickness or failure.

Attributes

Health and fitness. Illness and health issues. Diet.

Employment and the employer. Service performed for others. Collective duties and responsibilities. Self-integration with the environment. Ideal working conditions.

Perfection anxiety. Ego stress. Self-judgement and introspection. Personal limitations.

Routine tasks and duties. Skills or training acquired. Jobs and Employments. Caretaking. Maintenance. Discrimination. Apprenticeship.

Pets and small domestic animals (we serve our pets).

7th – House of Partnerships

The seventh house cusp is also called the descendant. Since the descendent is opposite the ascendant, it shows what you lack for yourself. It illuminates our shadow or what we neglect to embody. Usually, we exteriorize this shadow, projecting these qualities onto another. This is why the seventh house is attributed to open enemies.

The seventh house deals with sustained relationships, which implies cooperation and sharing with other persons.

Attributes

What we attract in a relationship. Attraction to qualities we admire from the other partner. Dealing with people one to one. Close, confidante-like relationships. Agreements and treaties. Marriages. Partnerships. Contracts. Open enemies.

Our projections and shadow. The other.

8th – House – House of Sex, Death, and Rebirth

The eighth house is where we experience the need to change and transform. Whenever we inhibit our ability to change, we die because we cannot grow. In the eighth house, we die so we can be reborn. The eighth house symbolizes sex, the cessation of thought, coping with the physical deaths of others, as well as reproduction, death, birth, and change. These are all biological imperatives that accelerate evolution.

The eighth house also includes assets of partners and inheritance. It is the support we receive from others.

Attributes

The breaking of attachments, hence death, changes, transformations. Transformation essential to growth. Sexual relationships and deeply committed relationships. Intimacy. Shared emotion, soul, and spiritual levels. Regeneration. Self-transformation.

The transcendence with something greater than one's self. Expansion of world view and the exchange, regeneration, and transmutation of one's vital energies.

Joint funds. Finances. Other person's resources. Inheritance. Hidden legacies. Business. Occult matters. Values and support of others.

Secret desires, impulses, and instincts. Taboos. Sleep. Research and investigations.

Where you express truth.

9th – House of Philosophy

Experiences related to the ninth house are the search for the meaning of things. It is the house of philosophy, religion, and legal matters. It refers in general to whatever expands a person's perspective or consciousness, such as long journeys, close contacts with other cultures, and with foreigners in general.

Attributes

Philosophy. Religion. Culture. Point of view. Perspective and belief systems. Spiritual orientation. Metaphysics and personal beliefs.

Law. Morals. Ethics. Higher education. Experience through expansion. Hope. Optimism.

The abstract or symbolic mind. Universities and higher education. Publishing. Broadcasting.

Long journeys. Foreign travel and languages. Adventure.

10th – House of Social Status and Career

The tenth house cusp is the mid-heaven or Medium Coeli, meaning *the middle of the sky*. It is the very top of the natal chart and represents where we meet the public. In the tenth house, we achieve success or failure in gaining a social position. It is where we assume the responsibility for our social and spiritual identity.

The tenth house tests our ability to *perform* our vocation or social office. Tenth house issues test our ability to be trusted with power.

Attributes

Position. Honor. Authority and status. Political power. Recognition. Career/Vocation. What you are called to do. The office you hold. What you give to the world. Public image and career.

Ambitions. Motivations. What needs recognition. How success is defined. Achievements. Awards.

The parent who represents authority. Father. Fatherhood. Government. Authority. Boundaries. Rules. Discipline.

Social participation. The discovery of one's spiritual identity.

Structures. Corporations. Tradition.

The 11th House Belonging and Blessings

The eleventh house symbolizes how we make friends and our attitudes towards non-emotional relationships. It is the house of our hopes, wishes, and membership in organizations and fraternities.

Attributes

Money obtained through your profession. Wealth.

Friendships. Teams. Fraternities. Volunteering. Social life. Social rules and lessons. Circle of friends. The groups we are members of. Fitting into society. Progressive politics and social reform.

Connectedness. Networking. Social media. Belonging. All-inclusive love.

Hopes and wishes. Collective ideas. Benefits from our efforts.

Originality. Sudden and unexpected events. Science fiction and futuristic.

12th – House of Mystery and Hidden Enemies

The twelfth house corresponds to the mythical underworld. It is a source of our hidden strengths, enemies, and limitations.

The twelfth and final house rules endings. It symbolizes the final stage of a project, tying up loose ends, completions, and spiritual debts to be repaid. The twelfth house is also associated with the afterlife, old age, and surrender.

The twelfth house symbolizes separation from society, institutions, hospitals, jails, hidden agendas, and secret enemies.

It symbolizes the subconsciousness, imagination, and creativity.

Attributes

Fate. Obstacles. Confinement. Karma. Subconscious states. The unconscious, both individual and collective. Dreams. Retreat. Reflection.

Losing boundaries. Unification. Depository for hidden repressions. Conflicts between the individual and society. Accumulated resources, both positive and negative.

Self-undoing (shooting ourselves in the foot). Hidden enemies. Blindspot. Things that are not apparent to self, yet clearly seen by others.

What requires withdrawal to integrate. Refuge from the world. The inner experiences that bring one to social independence.

Places of seclusion such as hospitals, mental hospitals, prisons, and institutions, including self-imposed imprisonments. Frustrations.

Martyrdom. Self-sacrifice. Suicide.

Mysticism and mystery. Elusive. Clandestine. Secretive matters. Privacy. Behind the scenes action.

Chapter 8

The Ascendant and Chart Ruler

The Ascendant is located on the left-hand side of the chart. It is the *sign and degree* on the first house cusp. The Ascendant is called the rising sign because it is the sign rising on the horizon at birth. To understand the ascendant, we need to revisit astrological houses.

Placidus House – Equinox – 7:06 AM

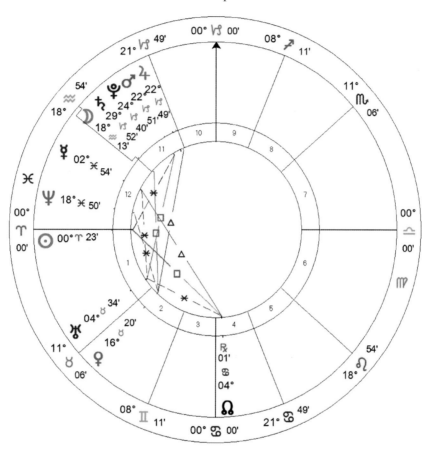

In the chart above, the is Sun rising (20 March 2020 at 7:06 AM, Denver Colorado) on the Equinox using the *Placidus house* system. Notice that the Sun is rising in the first degree of Aries. There are 30 degrees in each sign. The first degree is from 0 degrees and 1 minute to 0 degrees and 59 minutes. For Example,

	From	To
1st degree	0° 1'	0° 59'
2nd degree	1° 0'	1° 59'
3rd degree	2° 0'	2° 59'

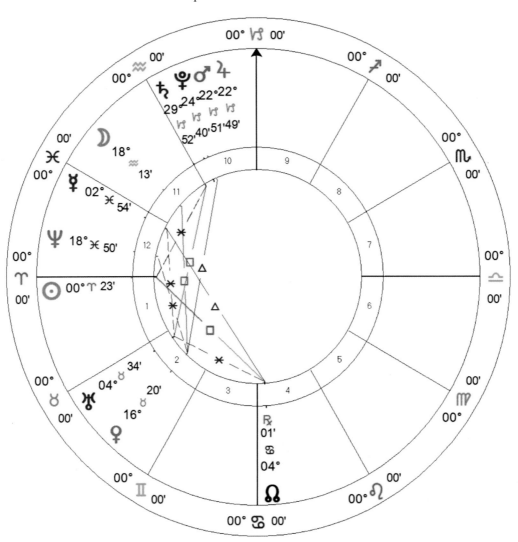

The equal house system means that every house is thirty degrees.

North of the Arctic Circle, the Sun sometimes doesn't rise or set for a few weeks, and so determining ascendant, and houses in the Placidus and other unequal house systems are problematic. In these cases, equal house systems are better charts.

The above charts are *natural charts* because Aries is on the first house cusp. However, all charts are not natural. The chart below has a Taurus Ascendant.

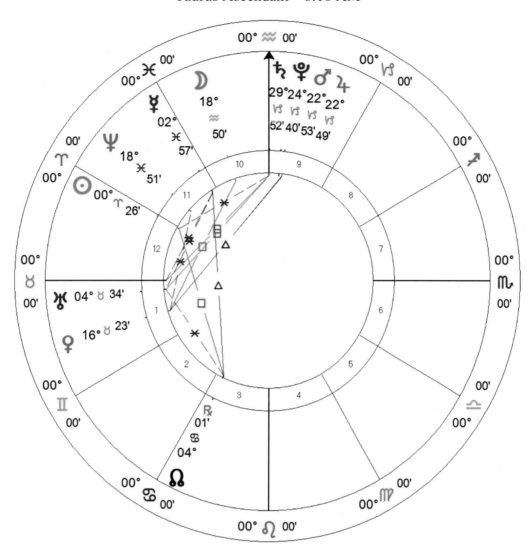

There are 24 hours in a day and 12 houses. Therefore, about every two hours, the sign on the ascendant changes. There are 120 minutes in two hours and 30 degrees in a sign. Hence, *every four minutes, the degree of the ascendant changes*. This is *one degree of oblique ascension* because the ecliptic is at an angle to Earth's axis of rotation. The slant (oblique ascension) varies depending on the latitude or how far north or south you are from the equator.

The equal house chart above is for 8:18 AM, which is one hour and 12 minutes later than the Aries chart above. This is less than the average of two hours in a sign.

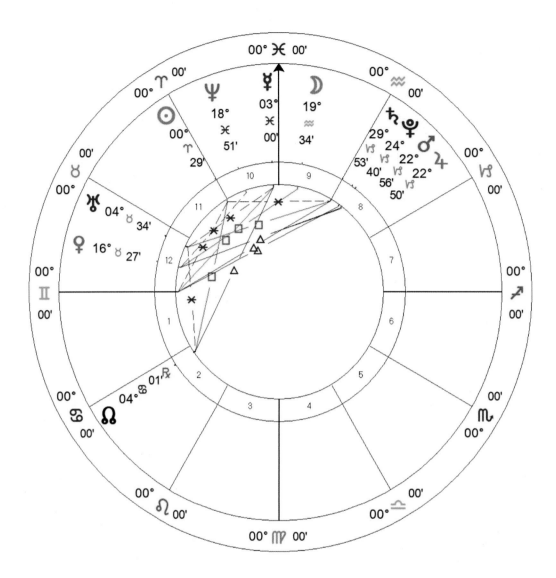

Back to the chart for Denver Colorado, 20 March 2020.

This chart is for 9:46:53 AM. The last two numbers are seconds. I use this notation because you will see it in astrological programs.

The difference between Taurus to Gemini rising is 1 hour and 29 minutes.

Notice how the planets are rotating clockwise.

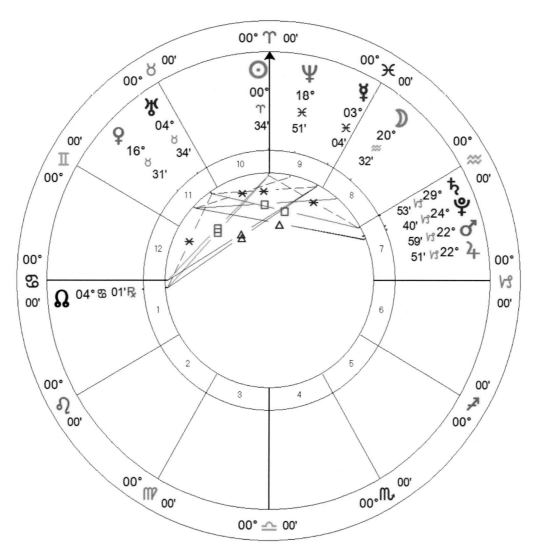

This chart is for 11:4O:38 AM.

When the sun was rising, the Moon was in 18°♒14' (18 degrees and 14 minutes Aquarius). At 9:46:53 AM, the Moon is 20°♒32'.

On average, the Sun, Mercury, and Moon move a degree a day. The Moon is a speedster at just over half a degree per hour, which is approximately equal to its apparent size. In a day, the Moon moves an average of 13.2 degrees.

The difference between Gemini to Cancer rising is 1 hour and 56 minutes.

Leo Ascendant – 2:02 PM

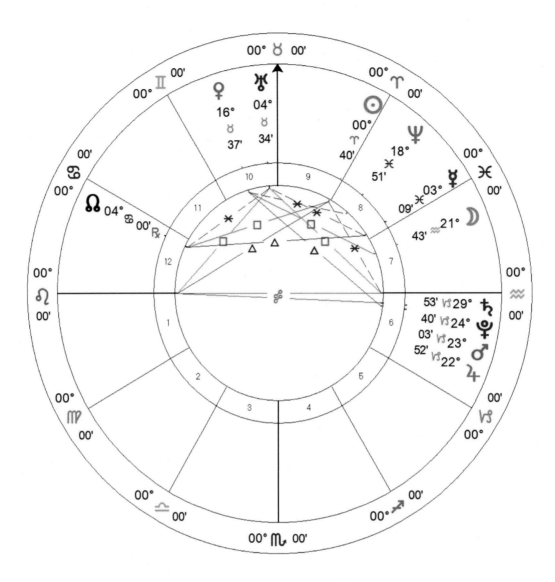

Saturn, Pluto, Mars, and Jupiter have set. They are below the horizon.

The time between Cancer to Leo rising is 2 hours and 21 minutes.

Virgo Ascendant – 4:34 PM

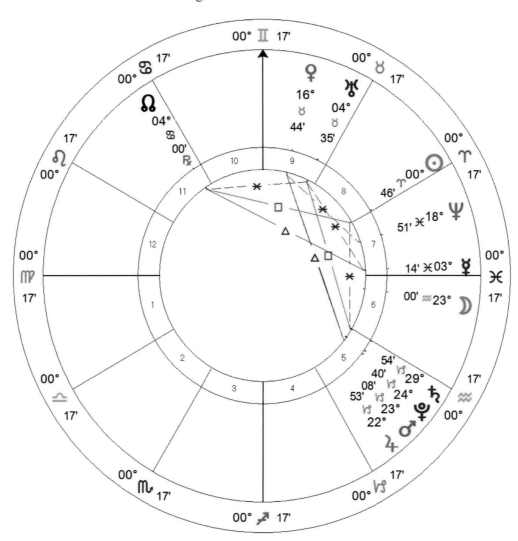

The Moon has set, and Mercury will be soon below the horizon or descendant.

The time between Leo to Virgo rising is 2 hours and 32 minutes.

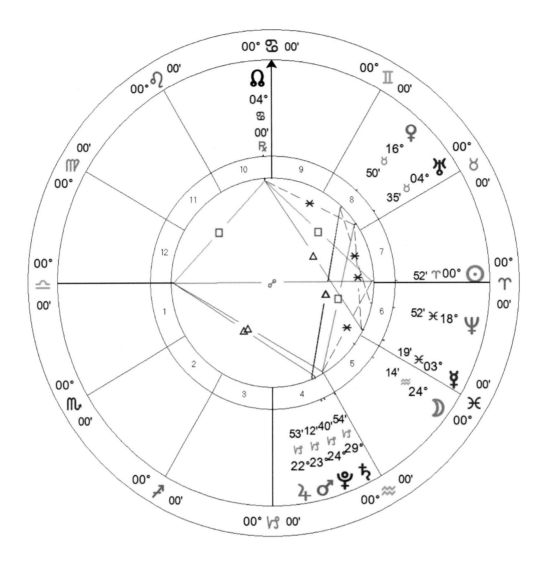

Libra Rising – 7:04 PM

The Sun began the day as 00°23' Aries. And very soon the Sunsets in 00°52' Aries.

The difference between Virgo to Libra rising is 2 hours and 30 minutes.

Now that we understand the mechanics of a birth chart, we can talk more about the ascendant.

The Ascendant in a Birth Chart

The Ascendant symbolizes our personality or ego. It shapes our attitude, first impressions, and appearance.

As children, we are shaped by life experiences and our relations with family members. Our individual expression is modified and conditioned by our need for recognition, particularly from our mothers and fathers. We adapt to our environment. Therefore, the rising sign indicates our life experiences and how we respond to different situations.

The ascendant is also called "mask" people wear. The personality is our protection (mask) worn in public and is similar to the meaning of Key 8, the Chariot.

From one perspective, the Charioteer is the Soul or Sun. The Chariot is the personality (the ascendant) which is the vehicle for the Soul.

Ascendant Attributes

Individuality. The personality. Ego. Our behavior. The way we act—the mask or persona we use to shield ourselves from the world. Our expression conditioned by the need for recognition. What we show the world.

+   The creative expression of Spirit.

-    Habitual behavior we use to keep others from getting close to us.

Chapter 9

The Luminaries

The luminaries are the Sun and Moon. They are the most important symbols in a natal chart. From one perspective, the Sun symbolizes self-consciousness and the father. The Moon is Subconsciousness and the mother. How these two luminaries interact by sign and aspect indicates the individual's relationship with their parents and how they respond to stress. This will be explored further in a later chapter.

The Sun

☉

The Sun is a symbol of our creative life force and our conscious mind. It is the power behind our will to live, be an individual, and meet life challenges. The Sun provides the individual with different experiences to discover our true nature.

Our Sun sign is the internal Adult. The Sun listens to the planets' input, but the Sun is the ruler.

Sun Attributes

Sense of individuality. Creative energy, radiant inner self (attunement of soul). Essential values. The urge to be and create. The need to be recognized and to express yourself. The source of will, vitality, and personal power. Qualities of leadership and authority. The center and power of self. The person's purpose and direction in life. The Soul. Life-force. Overall strength in life. The core sense of identity. Self-confidence. Important regarding women's relationships with men.

+   Radiation of spirit. Creative and loving pouring forth of self. Confidence. Leadership. Strength. Charisma. Creativity. Spontaneity.

-    Boastfulness. Pride. May adopt a false sense of life-purpose to try and please the father. Crisis in life-purpose. Feeling of unwanted or unloved. Lack of direction. Excessive desire to be special can lead to self-importance and arrogance.

The Moon

)

The Moon is our internal child. The Moon represents our feelings, especially those that are difficult to put into words. It also represents how we nurture ourselves. The lunar force is responsible for our emotional growth and maturity, as well as personal happiness.

The Moon indicates our mothers' influence or absence. Our mothers taught us how to meet our needs. The Moon conveys the way we generally relate to women and the female company we keep.

The Moon is our unconscious reactive habit patterns. Under stress, we instinctively do those things that nurture us to make us feel emotionally safe and secure. In our society, one of how we nurture ourselves is to spend money. A fourth house Moon may spend money on the home, a seventh mouse Moon spends money on its relationships, and a second house Moon saves money.

When the Moon is neglected or denied, our emotions can turn into depression or despair, telling us that something important is missing from our lives.

Moon Attributes

The subconscious. Mom and early childhood life. Unconscious reactive habit patterns. Primary emotional needs. Instinctive behaviors that we adopt to get love. Survival instincts. The familiar and comforting. Emotional style. How we satisfy ourselves. Attachment and dependency. Happiness and addictions. Ego-investment and defensiveness. How basic needs are met. Relations with women in general. The Mother Goddess archetype. A woman's maternal style. Reactions. Feeling-instinct responses. Adaptation to life experiences. Providing oneself with nourishment, protection, and assistance. Affection. Touching. Closeness. Capacity to trust. Ability to connect and be intimate. Food. Psychological patterns that arise during infancy. Bodily health.

+	Responsiveness. Inner contentment. Flowing, adaptable sense of self. The ability to reach out and care, nurture.

-	Isolated and separated from others. Feelings of guilt that one isn't giving enough. Sensitive to betrayal. Avoidance behavior. Emotional inhibition. Childhood humiliation. Oversensitivity. Insecurity. Inaccurate, inhibiting sense of self.

Chapter 10

The Personal Planets

Personal planets are the ones that embody our personality, basic drives, and motivations. The Sun, Moon, Mercury, Venus, and Mars are personal planets. The two luminaries, the Sun and Moon, are the most personal planets.

MERCURY

Mercury rules our communication style and impersonal thought processes. Mercury symbolizes intellectual development. The intellect's specialty is to figure things out and solve problems.

Mercury represents our ability to perceive and communicate. Mercury desires to express our perceptions and intelligence through skill or speech.

Mercury Attributes

The conscious mind (logical or rational mind). How we communicate, think, and process information. The development of intellect. Thinking and speaking style. Conceptual intelligence. Symbolic understanding. How we figure things out. How we solve problems. The Messenger archetype. Where (house) and how (sign) we need to talk. Conversational method. Comprehension and logical processes. The intellectual and reasoning quality of the person.

+   Creative use of skill or intelligence. Reason and power of discrimination. Ability to agree with objective understanding and clear verbal expression.

-      Misuse of skill or intelligence. Amorality through rationalization. Opinionated and one-sided communication. Deceit. Introversion. Lacking confidence in communication and expressing ideas.

VENUS

Venus is inspired when we are in partnership and romantic situations. By our communion and closeness with others, we establish values to create comfort and harmony in our relationships and environment. Through relationships, Venus expresses its internal experiences as emotions and affections.

When Venus is betrayed or neglected, we lose heart; we alienate ourselves by forbidding intimacy, relationship, and love.

Venus also symbolizes the creative imagination and the arts.

In a man's chart, Venus represents the type of women he finds attractive or how he feels about women. In a women's chart, it indicates her female ego and body acceptance.

Venus Attributes

Values. Tastes. Sharing. What we like. Personal love. Romance. Relationship patterns. How we attract intimacy. How beauty is defined. Personal aesthetics and tastes. What is pleasing to us. How we make ourselves attractive. Early imprints around love. Self-acceptance and worth. The Goddess of Love. Female sexuality and sexual attraction. Affairs of the Heart. Harmony. Art. Beauty. Affection. The ability to attract others and maintain relationships. Emotionally-colored tastes. Ability to relate, express love, and appreciate others — the ability to touch and be touched.

+   Love. Talents. Give and take with others. Sharing. The generosity of spirit.

-    Self-indulgence. Greed. Envy. Jealousy. Emotionally demanding. Inhibitions of affections. Misogyny. Idealistic about women. Unworthy of love. Feeling ugly, unloved, or unattractive.

MARS

Mars represents action, impulses, and sexual drive or libido. It motivates us to action and symbolizes all beginnings and release of energy.

In traditional astrology, Mars is a malefic. He is the warrior and soldier archetype. Mars tends toward conflict and aggression. The sign that Mars is in can indicate the things that make us angry. For example, Mars in Libra gets angry when people are not treated fairly.

A denied Mars dissipates motivation, the will to act, and physical and sexual vitality. When we suppress the Mars force, our aggressive tendencies go inward and can manifest as accidents or injuries.

For a man, it is often connected with his male ego, sexuality, and vigor. In a women's chart, it will often indicate the type of man she is attracted to or how she feels about men.

Mars Attributes

The principles of energy, force, will, desire, and passion. Sexuality. The will to act. Initiative. Physical energy. Force and might. Drive to initiate action. What gets me angry how we fight. The manifestation of initiative, assertion, and aggression. How we assert ourselves. Sex drive. Penetration. How we go about getting what we want. Motivation. The sexual promise. Muscular system. Physical needs of the body. Action. The Warrior archetype. Will power. Mating behavior. What we learn to fight for. Where you expend the most energy. Ability to survive in the world. Self-defense and aggression. Self-assertion. Dealing with conflict, competition. Conflict resolution.

+   Courageous. Initiative. Willpower consciously directed toward a legitimate aim.

-       Impatience. Willfulness. Violence. Improper use of force or threats. Difficulty expressing anger. Problems with authority figures. Childhood abuse. Promiscuity. Difficulty in gathering energy to get things done. Procrastination.

Chapter 11

Social Planets, Transpersonal Planets, and the Moon Nodes

The social planets, Jupiter and Saturn, represent the individual's connection to the public and organizations, such as governments and religions. Personal planets are imbodied by the individual, while social planets usually manifest through other people or established institutions.

JUPITER - ♃

Jupiter is a greater fortune in astrology. Our fortune is the culmination of our actions and thoughts to the present moment. The fortune we created can be either positive or negative, depending on our deeds.

Jupiter symbolizes the expansion of consciousness, sometimes through hardships. Jupiter is attributed to law, scientific research, philosophy, and religion. All these are human activities where we seek to expand our horizons through interactions with other people.

Jupiter is associated with religion, law, and philosophy. Mercury brings knowledge, Jupiter can bring wisdom.

Jupiter Attributes

The principle of expansion, opportunity, success, prosperity, and growth. What draws you out and gives optimism. Social laws. Cooperation. Civilization. How I seek to grow and trust in life. Consciousness expansion. Point of view and perspective. Beliefs. Opportunistic aptitudes. What is amplified by faith. Intuition. Risk-taking. Morality and code of ethics. Deals and gambles. Support. Protection. Generosity. Abundance. Intuition. Religion.

+   Hope. Faith. Charity. Wisdom. Benevolence. Generous. Social opportunities. Exploration. Widening horizons. Optimism. Growth. Justice. Opportunity. Fortune and abundance. Reliance on a higher power or greater plan and, therefore, lucky. Openness to grace.

-     Over-confidence. Self-righteousness. Laziness. Leaving the work to others. Irresponsibility. Miserly. An atmosphere of poverty. Low self-esteem. Over-extending self or promising too much. Difficulty recognizing limits.

SATURN – ♄

Saturn represents authority, formal organizations, and our ability to focus and restrict our activities. Saturn shows us where we can be our most effective and competent through our hard work.

Saturn is a malefic planet. He exposes our shortcomings and defects, where we lack personal experience and emotional development. Therefore, the house that Saturn dwells indicates where we may have issues of inadequacy. For example, a first house Saturn thinks they're not good enough, a third house Saturn thinks they're not intelligent enough, and an eight house Saturn can fear intimacy.

Saturn Attributes

The principles of contraction, limitation, restriction, and discipline. Sorrow and hardships. Area of greatest tribulations and challenges. The father and authority issues. Administrators. Work. Effort. Karma. The principle of form and definition. Motivation through fear. No pain, no gain. How one seeks to establish and preserve self. Where effort, hard work, and responsibility are required to succeed. Ambition. Infantile wound. Shortcoming and defects. Fears. Commitments. Responsibilities. Being your own parent. Long term endurance. What you want the most and the fear of failure. Fate (Saturn is the Lord of Karma). Commitment. Rules. Responsibility. Stability. Laws.

+   Self-discipline. Depth of thought. Maturity. Acceptance of duties and responsibilities. Patience. Perseverance. Organization. Reliability. Good-worker. Grounded. Stable. A sense of purpose.

-      Self-restriction. Procrastination. Stagnation. Rigidity. Coldness. Defensiveness. Negativity. Difficulties with authority and limitations. Hardship. Sorrow. Stress. Depression. Fears. Phobias. Misfortune. Unfair situations. Separation. Severing.

Trans-Personal Planets

The transcendental planets (those beyond the orbit of Saturn) represent newer energies that have been impacting this planet. In a sense, they are a natural outcome of humanity's successful integration of the seven inner planets. These planets co-rule Aquarius, Pisces, and Scorpio.

Planet		Co-Rules	
Uranus	♅	Aquarius	♒
Neptune	♆	Pisces	♓
Pluto	♇	Scorpio	♏

Due to the great distance from the sun, planets beyond Saturn have a long orbital period.

Planet		Orbit Period (years)	Time in sign (years)
Uranus	♅	84	7
Neptune	♆	165	14
Pluto	♇	248	21

Since a trans-personal planet stays in one sign for several years, it colors the consciousness of an entire generation. For example, Uranus is in Taurus from March 2019 to July 2025. Taurus rules money and banks. During this period, I expect the governments and banks will grumble their acceptance of bitcoins and other virtual money.

Since Uranus, Neptune, and Pluto are trans-personal planets, they can have indirect effects on our lives unless they are aspected by one of the personal planets. For example, with Pluto conjunct the Sun, the individual will be dealing with Pluto on a day to day basis to discover more out their true nature.

However, if Pluto isn't aspecting a personal planet, the effects are felt through the house that Pluto resides. *If any planet falls withing four degrees of a house cusp, their influence will be particularly potent.*

Uranus – ♅

Mercury represents the personal mind. Uranus is the collective mind or mind of God. Uranus represents the need for freedom, originality, and liberation.

Uranus can manifest inspired knowledge and experiences as well as disruption and instability to your environment and personality. These experiences can have an electrical quality that is sudden and unpredictable.

Uranus dislikes *externally* imposed restrictions that hinder its expression. Uranus requires *internally* imposed conditions to bring into manifestation its ideas. Uranus' brilliant streak needs to follow its own rules to manifest its genius.

Attributes

The higher octave of Mercury. Sudden changes and crises. Disruption. Chaos and new possibilities. Revolutionary. Instability. Genius and Eccentricity. Originality. Unique. Inventiveness. Innovation. Waking up. Akashic records. True autonomy. Where freedom is required to function (by house and sign). Rebels against externally-imposed restrictions. Electrical, sudden, intermittent, and unpredictable. Personal audacity. Discontinuity and detachment. Creative and destructive chaos. Freedom. Liberation. Interest in astrology or metaphysics. Divine discontent. Technology. Psyche-shattering events.

+   Attunement to the truth. Originality. Inventiveness. Directed experimentation. Respect for freedom & individuality. Brilliant.

-    Willfulness. Restless impatience. A constant need for excitement and purposeless change. Rebellion. Extremism. Odd. Crazy. A rebel without a cause. Impatient with restriction.

Neptune - Ψ

Neptune is the higher octave of Venus. Venus as personal love, while Neptune is the Love of God or unconditional love. Love is a unifying force. Neptune dissolves ego boundaries so that we may be released from the confines of the personal self. It is the urge to escape from the limitations of one's self and the material world. Therefore, Neptune rules mysticism, meditational practices, as well as drugs.

Neptune is idealistic. Non-realized ideals or unrealistic goals lead to a disillusionment that can leave the individual bitter.

Neptune can seek to escape the thralldom of matter, especially with natal Neptune aspecting the Sun or Moon.

Alcoholism, a Neptunian dissolving disease, can occur with strong aspects and transits to Neptune.

Neptune Attributes

The higher octave of Venus. Unconditional love. Compassion. Dreams and visions. The principle of unification and transcendence. Urge to return to harmony and unity. Service and self-sacrifice. Escapism. Psychic phenomena. Escape into the formless and irrational. Where we disappear. No boundaries. Imagination. Impressibility. Nebulousness. Art. Music. Mysticism. Charity. Religion. The intangible. Martyrdom. Merging. Uniting.

+   Attunement with the whole. Realization of the spiritual dimension of experience. Universal compassion. Living an ideal. Ability to see good in people. Contemplation. Service orientated.

-       Confusion. Escapism. Deception. Drugs. Addictions. Evasion of responsibilities. Refusal to face one's motives and to commit to anything. High ideals and expectations, and therefore disillusionment. Paranoia. Persecution. Megalomania. Messiah complex. Delusions of grandeur. Lack of boundaries. Lack of faith.

Pluto - ♇

Pluto represents the principles that something must die for something new to take its place. The personality must die to the old to be infused with the Power of the Soul.

Pluto eliminates and purifies all that it touches. Pluto rules the unconscious mind, deep instincts, and the underworld. It represents the power to create, destroy, and the power of radical transformation and revolution.

Pluto's powerful transformative force can turn into an obsession. For example, in the seventh house, Pluto gets obsessed with relationships.

Pluto is co-ruler with Mars with the sign of Scorpio. Pluto is considered the higher octave of Mars. If Mars is personal, Will, then Pluto would be the Cosmic Will or the Will of God.

Pluto remains in a zodiacal sign for many years, and as a result, it primarily represents the style of a generation. The house Pluto dwells in your chart can bring a spiritual crisis. Its placement points to where the greatest change takes place in our lives as well as where things are destroyed if we don't take care of ourselves.

Pluto Attributes

The principal of elimination & purification of toxins. Spiritual regeneration. Metamorphosis. Cleaning. Healing. Taboos and secrets. Telling the truth. Transformation. Death and Rebirth. Deep shock and spiritual crisis. Area of greatest change. Soul Intent. Obsession and compulsive acts. Spiritual awakening and healing. Powers of rejuvenation. Utilization of power. Sexual/spiritual fusion. Transformation through elimination and destruction. Surrender. Letting go. Domination. Fear of being devoured. Seduction. A Phoenix rising out of the ashes.

+   Ability to surrender to a higher power. Ability to dissolve attachments.

-       Obsessiveness. Addictive over-indulgence. Manipulation. Vampirism. Controlling. Projection of inner need for change onto others. Misuse of power. When neglected, The loss of soul and personal power.

The Moon's Nodes

☊ - ☋

The Moon's nodes are not planets, but abstract points. In astronomy, the rising node (☊ - North Node) is the point where the Moon crosses the ecliptic (the path of the Sun as seen from Earth) from south to north. The descending node (☋ - South Node) is where it crosses from north to south. The North Node is called the dragon's head, and the South Node the dragon's tail. The dragon in mythology is the beast devours the Sun and causes Solar eclipses.

The two nodes are 180° apart and retrograde. For example, if the North Node is in five degrees Aries, the South Node is 5 degrees Libra. The two nodes are inseparable.

In tropical (western) astrology, there are several variations of meaning:

1. The North is considered helpful and has properties similar to Jupiter. The South Node has properties similar to Saturn.

2. The North Node is your Darma or path of the soul. The South Node is your personal Karma.

3. The North Node is what you are here to learn, and the South Node is what you bring in from previous lifetimes.

4. The sign and house placement of the North Node represent circumstances and activities that are unfamiliar. The sign and house placement of the South Node tell where you are inclined to overdo things.

5. In Vedic astrology (Jyotish), both nodes are problematic.

Ezra's *Introductions to Astrology* says,

The Ancients said that the nature of the Head of the Dragon is to increase and the nature of the tail is to decrease; therefore, if benefic planets are with the Head of the Dragon it increases their good fortune, and if malefic planets are with the Head of the dragon, it increases their misfortune.

And if benefic planets are with the Tail of the Dragon, it decreases their good fortune, and if malefic planets are with the Tail of the Dragon, it decreases their misfortune. – p. 187.

Chapter 12

Aspects

An aspect is a specific number of degrees of separation between two planets. By counting zodiacal signs (not houses), we can determine the type of aspect, if any, is formed.

In this book, the aspects used are conjunction, sextile, trine, square, and opposition. There are others, but before learning the minor ones, be proficient in the major aspects. Technically, the conjunction is not an aspect. It's a blending of the two planetary energies.

Aspect			Type	Keywords
Conjunction	☌	0°	Mixed	Merging energies. Stress
Sextile	*	60°	harmonious	Opportunity. Luck
Square	□	90°	challenging	Challenges. Order. Decision making. Reason.
Trine	△	120°	harmonious	Talent. Ease. Flow. Harmonious interaction.
Opposition	☍	180°	challenging	Awareness. Duality. Self & not-self.

△ – Trine – 120°

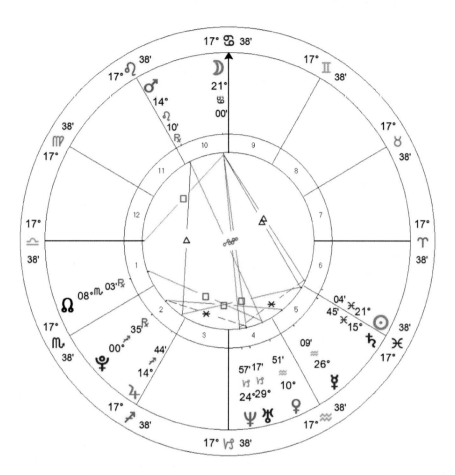

In the chart above (11 March 1995, 8:11 PM), the Moon is 21 degrees 0 minutes Gemini (21°Ⅱ00'), and the Sun is 21 degrees and 4 minutes Aquarius (21°♒04'). Gemini and Aquarius are Air signs. Counting the signs from Aquarius is Pisces-Aries-Taurus-Gemini. Thirty degrees times four is 120 degrees. The Moon is a faster-moving planet that's moving towards the Sun. The angular distance from a perfect trine is called orb. Therefore, this aspect is an *applying trine* with an *orb* of 4 minutes.

The trine gives talent, ease, creativity, and help to affected planets. However, the trine needs stimulation, or it leads to laziness and inertia, with the native content to do nothing but receive the benefits of the trine. The challenging aspects that interact with the trine motivate the planets to action.

Ezra says, *two planets in trine are like two persons with the same nature.*

Attributes

Flow and ease. Harmony. Talents. Unchallenged. Comfortable.

Grand Trine

The grand trine is formed with three planets that are spaced approximately 120° apart. Due to the close circuit of energy formed by this aspect, the orb can be extended somewhat from that of a normal trine. They are usually but not always in the same element. When they are, the planets involved are linked to one another for a purpose symbolized by the element involved.

Grand Trines represent talent and self-sufficiency. The type of talent is symbolized by the element and planets that form a grand trine. Generally speaking:

Fire Trine: Inspiration, intuition, visionary, forceful. Courageous. Ability to act alone.

Water Trine: Emotional self-sufficiency.

Air Trine: Intellectual strength and dexterity. Intellectual self-sufficiency.

Earth Trine: Practical material self-sufficient. Resourceful people.

However, talents can be two-edged swords. When things come too easy, we take it for granted. We may to be lazy and not develop this talent. The ease and self-sufficiency associated with a grand trine may make it difficult for us to communicate with others. For example, a grand water trine may seem unapproachable emotionally. A grand air trine may be so sure of their opinion that they forget it is just an opinion. A Grand Fire trine can be arrogant and willful in pursuit of their goals. Earth Grand Trines material self-sufficiency may make it difficult for them to share. Isolation is the keyword that can describe unintegrated grand trines.

Grand Air Trine

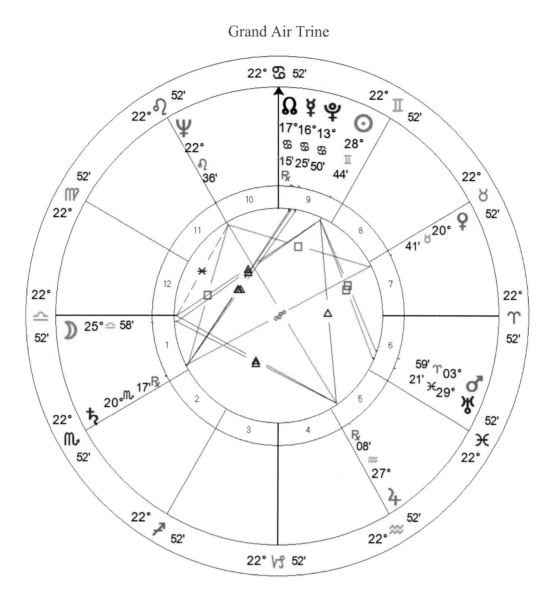

In the Chart above (20 June 1926, 2:01 PM), the Sun, Moon, and Jupiter form a grand air trine. Mars and Neptune form a square to the Sun, and Neptune is in opposition to Jupiter. The hard aspects stimulate the planets in the grand air trine to action.

☐ - Square – 90°

A square is formed by two planets that are three signs away from each other.

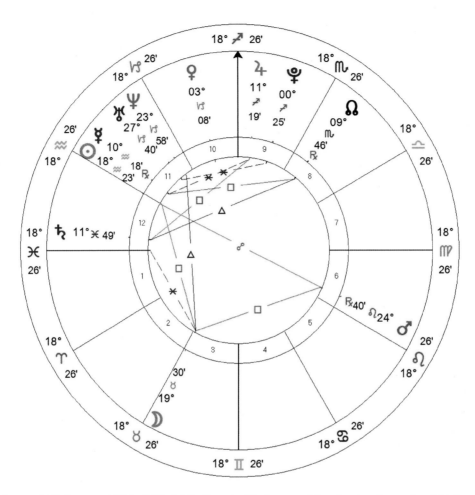

In the chart above (7 February 1995, 8:23 AM), Sun is 18 degrees 23 minutes Aquarius (Air), and the Moon is 19 degrees 30 minutes Taurus (Earth). The angular separation between the two luminaries is 91 degrees and 7 minutes. The moon is the faster planet and is forming a *separating square* with an *orb* of 1 degree and 7 minutes (1°7'). The more exact the aspect, the stronger it is in the natal chart.

The square or ninety-degree aspect indicates conflicting needs between the two planets. They symbolize problems and points of tension in the native. Although square aspects are often experienced as painful events, they motivate us to improve ourselves and undergo evolution and growth. They are stumbling blocks, but they are also building blocks of future development.

Dane Rudhyar describes a square as a *crisis of decision*. Any crisis involves the choice among alternatives, leaving some, and embracing others. When major life decisions do come in the forms of crisis, it is often an indication that some decision has not been taken. When we fail to decide, it often comes back to haunt us in a sharper form than if we decide out of ignorance or misunderstanding. Generally, squares in cardinal signs make quick decisions. Fixed signs are slow and calculating, while mutable squares are variable.

People with many squares, however, if they work hard at overcoming the conflicts, achieve remarkable personal growth and self-fulfillment, but it's a slog.

Ezra says, *Two planets in quartile (square) are like two persons who each seek rulership.*

Square Attributes

Conflict. The crisis of decision. Creative tension. Challenges. Dynamic action. Crisis and Action-oriented. Motivated. Willing to tackle obstacles. Strength of character and will.

A T Square is composed of three planets, two in opposition with one squaring both of them. The chart below is for 12 July 2020 (8:08 AM).

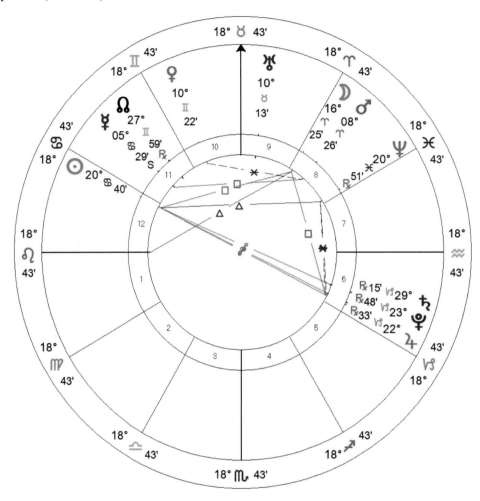

The Sun in Cancer, Moon in Aries, and Jupiter in Capricorn form a cardinal T-square.

An individual with a T Square undergoes periodic crisis or difficult decision making throughout their lives. Transits usually trigger crises to planets in the T square. The type of T cross (cardinal, fixed, or mutable) will set the tone of the decisions that are to be made, both by sign and house. The third planet at the midpoint (in this chart, the Moon) of the two oppositions usually acts as a release or externalization symbolized by the opposition.

For the chart above, when either Saturn, Pluto Jupiter, or Sun get triggered, the natural tendency is to retreat into 9th house activities. With a Moon in the ninth house, when the going gets tough, the tough goes on a road trip.

My teacher said that instead of doing the natural tendency, look to the opposite house for answers. In this chart, the opposite house of the ninth house moon is the third house. It is associated with brothers and sisters, writing, grade school, short journeys. Therefore, instead of traveling to far lands to meet new people when the T-square gets triggered, it's best to connect with a sibling, school mates, or read a book. Many successful people have a T-square in their chart.

Grand Cross

The Grand Cross needs to take action. Natives live with constant stress. The Grand Cross in a chart represents a person who cannot rest until their purpose is known. This aspect pulls the native in many directions that can create indecisiveness — any trines and sextiles to the planets in a grand cross aids in overcoming conflicts.

The Grand Fixed Cross or T Square

The Fixed mode seeks security and stability. A person with this aspect is concerned with giving structure and meaning to their lives. Any crystallized structures they built for stability get periodically shattered. Attention should be given to enduring values and being flexible.

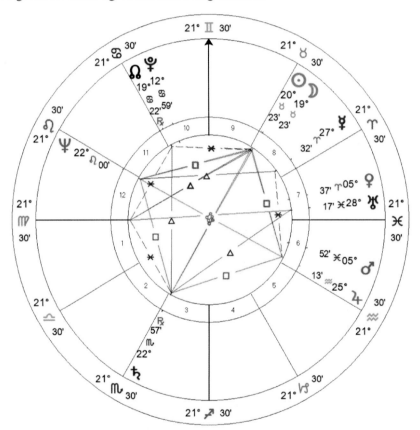

This chart is from 11 May 1926 (2:02 PM). Neptune, Saturn, Jupiter, Sun, and Moon from a grand fixed cross. Notice that all of the planets are in fixed signs.

Usually, a person with a fixed cross is well organized but has difficulty directing their talents. In the chart above, Pluto and Uranus are making a trine to Saturn. Pluto is also making a sextile to the Sun and Moon. These planets will ensure that the individual will not be stuck in a rut caused by indecision.

The Cardinal Grand Cross or T Square

The cardinal modality seeks to initiate action. An individual with a cardinal grand cross or T-square can be critical, impersonal, who is constantly searching for new things to do and to put their energies into operation. However, the individual may try to accomplish everything at the same time and have problems maintaining their focus.

The Mutable Cross or T Square

The mutable mode is changeable and adaptable. The individual must guard against being too adaptable to meet the needs of others and passing fads. T-squares and grand crosses in mutable signs dispose the individual to be concerned with people and intimate relationships.

☌ - Conjunction

A conjunction is two or three planets within 7 degrees of each other. They are usually in the same sign, but they don't have to be — for example, a planet 29° Cancer is still conjunct a planet 2° Leo.

Conjunctions represent the beginning of a new cycle. When a new cycle starts, the remnants of the old cycle is brought to a conclusion. There is an intensification of energy and activity with a conjunction, especially if it is an applying conjunction. The tighter the orb, the greater the emphasis the conjunction will have in the birth chart.

The planets involved will operate as a single unit and will act more strongly than they would alone. The conjunction will focus and concentrate energy and blend the forces the planets represent. This concentrated focus can lead to self-absorption or internal focus. Depending on the planets involved, conjunctions create a spontaneous activity that's more reactive than conscious.

Conjunctions in a chart will make the person more individualistic and self-centered. A conjunction can be problematic if the native is unable to see the other person's perspective.

Many conjunctions in a chart emphasize the house they reside in. Individuals with conjunctions are focused on and derive their motivation from within.

Conjunctions to Sun (combust), Mars, Saturn, Neptune, Uranus, Pluto are considered hard or stressful while conjunctions to Mercury, Venus, Moon, and Jupiter are easier.

Conjunction Attributes

Intensity. New beginning. Concentration. Focus of Power.

Ezra says, *two planets in conjunction are like two persons who meet.*

Stelliums

Stelliums are four or more planets are conjunct or if five or more planets located in the same sign. This chart is for 17 January 2020 (8:04 AM) with the five planets are in Capricorn and form a stellium. It suggests an individual with a strong focus on twelfth house issues.

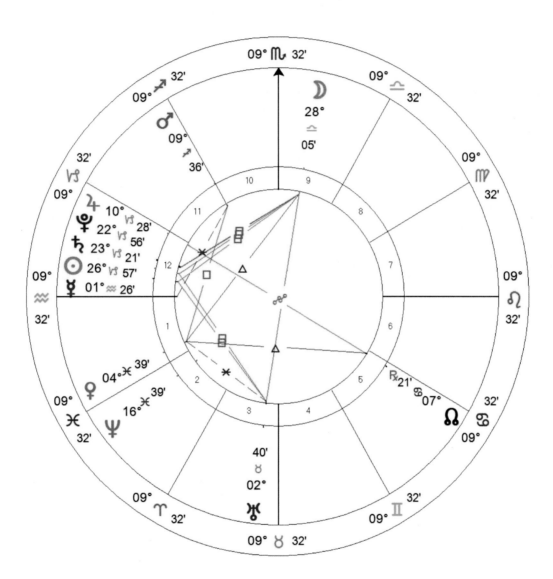

A sextile is formed by two planets that are two signs away from each other.

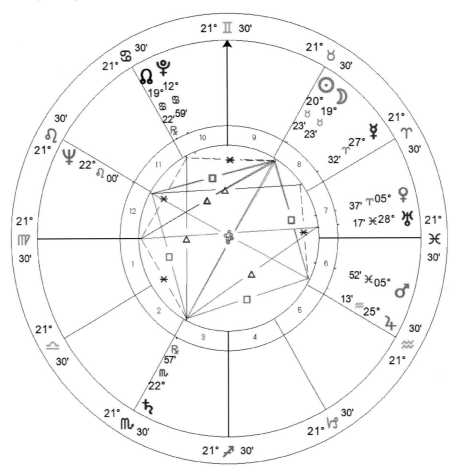

In the chart above, Mercury (27°♈32') in Aries (Fire) is sextile Jupiter (25°♒13') in Aquarius (Air). Both are active elements.

Earth signs sextile Water signs. Fire signs sextile Air signs. It is said that Air forms a container for Fire. Earth is the container of Water.

A sextile indicates the ability to draw upon and synthesize materials from many sources. It indicates hidden talents that can be developed.

Sextile Attributes

Opportunities. Attraction. Luck. Communicative. Creative. Expressive.

Ezra says, *two planets in sextile are like two persons who see each other's love.*

An opposition is formed by planets which are in opposite zodiacal signs or 180° apart.

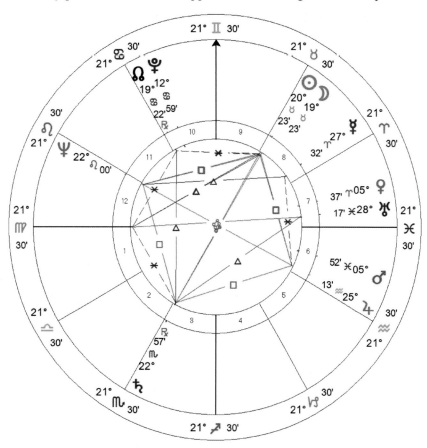

In the above chart, Saturn (22♏57') in Scorpio is in opposition with the Sun and Moon in Taurus. The table below lists the signs and their oppositions.

Aries	♈	Libra	♎
Taurus	♉	Scorpio	♏
Gemini	♊	Sagittarius	♐
Cancer	♋	Capricorn	♑
Leo	♌	Aquarius	♒
Virgo	♍	Pisces	♓

An opposition occurs on a full moon. This is when the Moon reflects the maximum amount of light from the Sun. Therefore, oppositions represent the highest level of contrast, complement, and development. An opposition sharpens the contrast between the two planets involved.

The most challenging oppositions occur between planets whose functions are polar – such as Sun/Moon, Sun/Saturn, Venus/Mars, Mercury/Jupiter, Jupiter/Saturn, Saturn/Uranus, Jupiter/Neptune, Pluto/Mars.

The opposition shares some of the characteristics of Libra and the 7th house. The opposition ties together compatible but different elements, producing awareness through separation, projection, and conflict.

Ezra says, *two planets in opposition are like two persons locked in fierce combat with each other.*

Opposition Attributes

Awareness. Understanding. Insightful. Conflict. Striving for balance. Raising of consciousness. Complementary forces. Contradictory. Seeks balance and growth through relationships.

Orb

The planets in a birth chart are rarely an exact aspect. The amount of variation from the aspect is called the *orb*.

In traditional astrology, the planets have orbs that are modified by the type of aspect — for example, the Sun trine Mars. The Sun is a luminary and has an orb of 12 degrees while Mars has 7 degrees for its orb. By adding 12 and 7 (19) and divide by two (10.5) is the orb of a Sun and Mars aspect. This is a detail that astrology programs do for charts.

The major aspects (conjunction, opposition, trine, square) are allowed a greater orb than minor aspect (sextile). The two luminaries (Sun and Moon) get larger orbs because they are the strongest factors in the chart while the other planets (Uranus, Neptune, and Pluto) get tighter orbs.

The table below gives the average values for major aspects. The minor aspects such as inconjunct and semi-square the orbs are much tighter.

Aspect		Average Orb	Orb of Sun & Moon	Outer Planets	Moon Nodes Ascendant & Mc
Conjunction	☌	7°	10°	5°	3 − 5
Sextile	*	5°	5°	5°	3 − 5
Square	□	7°	10°	5°	3 − 5
Trine	△	7°	10°	5°	3 − 5
Opposition	☍	7°	10°	5°	3 − 5

In Ezra's *Introductions to Astrology* (pp.231 − 233), he has this to say about the aspects.

Two planets in conjunction are like two persons who meet.

Two planets in sextile are like two persons who see each other's love.

Two planets in trine are like two persons with the same nature.

Two planets in quartile (square) are like two persons who each seek rulership.

Two planets in opposition are like two persons locked in fierce combat with each other.

Astrology programs do the heavy lifting and calculate the aspects and display them in a grid. Below is an example from the Solar Fire Program. Below is a chart for March 20, 2020

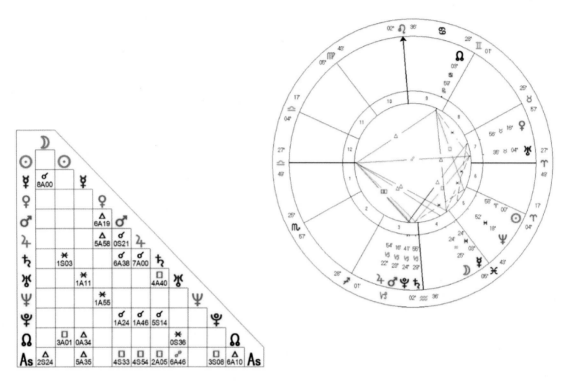

The second row from the top displays a conjunction between the Moon and Mercury. The "A" means its an *applying* conjunction.

Homework

Using your chart, fill out the aspect grid. Your chart probably came with an aspect grid filled out, but its good practice to write your aspects down.

☉										
☽										
☿										
♀										
♂										
♃										
♄										
♅										
♆										
♇										
	☉	☽	☿	♀	♂	♃	♄	♅	♆	♇

Chapter 13

The Relationships between the Sun, Moon and the Ascendant

There are many different ways to look at the luminaries. For example, the Sun is the self, but from another perspective, it's the soul, and sometimes it's the father. The Moon represents the subconsciousness, emotions, the mother, and women in general. The ascendant is personality and how Sun, Moon, and planets act out their passion play through our lives.

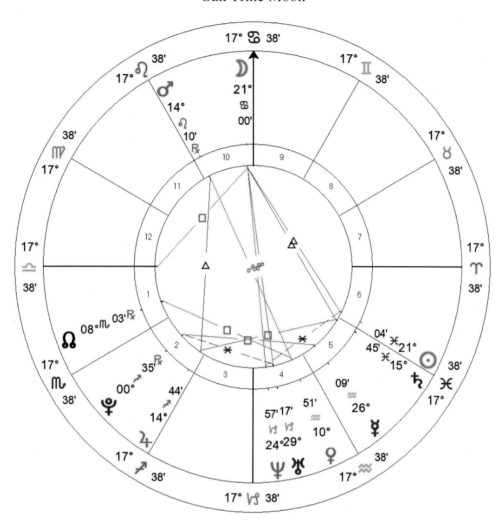

Considering the Sun is the father, and the Moon is the mother. In the chart above, there is a trine between these planets. I would expect the native experiences of the mother and father as a united front growing up. These experiences get incorporated into the native's personality, and so from another perspective, the self-conscious Sun and the subconsciousness Moon are in good communication. With both luminaries in air signs, they understand each other.

Air signs are active and communicative. However, the ascendant is Scorpio, a fixed water sign. Scorpio's are excellent poker players because they are good at keeping their emotions in check. When you meet a person for the first time, you see their ascendant. After you are friends, you get introduced to the Sun and Moon. I expect this person with this chart to be reserved until you get to know them.

Sun Square Moon

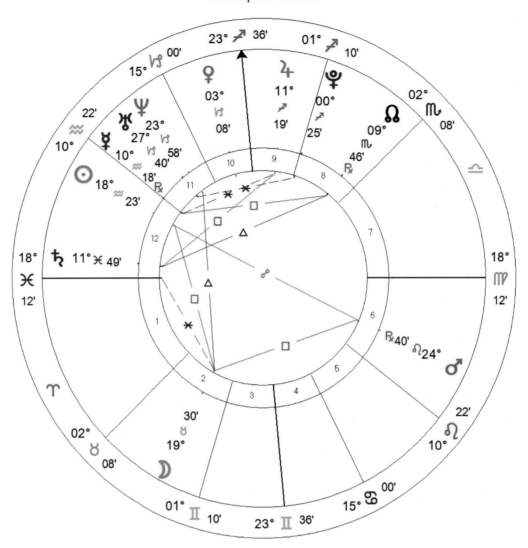

In the chart above (7 Feb 1995, 8:23 AM), the Sun is in Aquarius, Moon in Taurus, and Pisces ascendant. The Sun and Moon are square. The Moon casts a sextile to the ascendant. Technically, the Ascendant and Mid-heaven cannot cast an aspect. Instead, planets aspect these points. But this is no hard and fast rule.

Notice Pisces is a Water sign, and the Moon is in an Earth sign. Therefore, the personality and the Moon get along well. They understand each other. However, the Sun and Moon are at odds. The Sun is in Detriment in Aquarius while the Moon is Exalted in Taurus. In an argument, the Moon wins. The Sun in the twelfth house wants to retreat into his shell. The Moon from the second house prods him to make money.

Moon in Gemini

In the chart above, one of my students has Moon in Gemini. In an Air sign, the Moon likes to talk about her feelings. However, The Sun is in an Earth sign (Taurus), and the Sun is in Water (Pisces). These are introverted signs that are conservative and not inclined to share their feelings. The native said that whenever she talks about her feelings, later when she thinks about it, it was the "wrong thing to do."

The Sun, Moon and Ascendant and their relationships set the tone for our lives.

Chart Ruler

The planet that rules the astrological sign of the ascendant is called the chart ruler.

Ascendant		Chart Ruler	Ascendant		Chart Ruler
Aries	♈	♂	Libra	♎	♀
Taurus	♉	♀	Scorpio	♏	♂, ♇
Gemini	♊	☿	Sagittarius	♐	♃
Cancer	♋	☽	Capricorn	♑	♄,
Leo	♌	☉	Aquarius	♒	♄, ♅
Virgo	♍	☿	Pisces	♓	♃, ♆

Scorpio, Aquarius, and Pisces have co-rulers. Either planet can be a chart ruler, but usually, one planet has more emphasis. The planet that rules the natal chart can set the theme for the individual's life. For example, if the chart ruler is in the first house, the individual is a self-starter. They are good at taking the initiative. If the chart ruler is in the second house, the individual may define themselves through material possession, skills, and values. House Rulers is covered extensively in volume three of *The Only Way to Learn Astrology*.

Note the sign and house that the chart ruler resides. This planet, because of its association with the ascendant, has an additional emphasis in your chart. How much influence this planet will have depends on its placement by house, sign, and aspects to other planets. For this exercise, note your chart ruler and ask yourself how this planet operates in your chart.

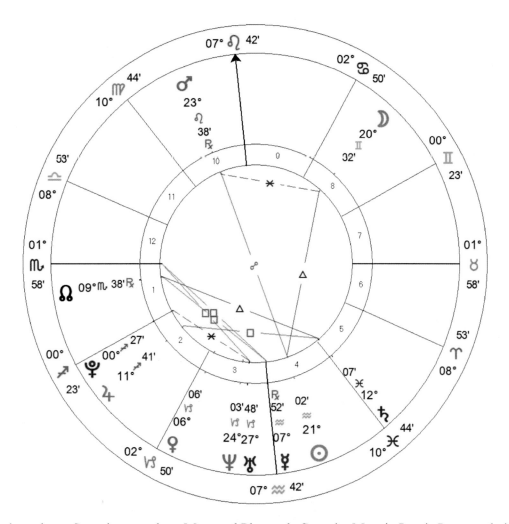

The chart above has a Scorpio ascendant. Mars and Pluto rule Scorpio. Mars in Leo is Retrograde in the tenth house. Mars makes an opposition to the Sun and a sextile to the Moon.

The Sun and Moon have a very nice relation by trine. Then Mars comes along and adds his biting comments to the Sun by opposition while he sweet talks to the Moon by sextile. Since Mars is retrograde, he can't do too much damage to the Sun/Moon relationship. Mars in the tenth house can be combative with the public, which can harm public reputation.

Pluto is in the second house, and it's not aspecting any of the personal planets. However, he is conjunct with the second house cusp by less than a degree. Notice that Jupiter rules Sagittarius and is dignified by Triplicity (see essential dignities). The second house rules finances so this individual can make and possibly lose a great deal of money.

These ideas set a theme for the chart. Chart rulers, as well as the Sun, Moon, and Ascendant relationships, develop the big picture, as well as the rising planet.

The planet nearest to the ascendant is the rising planet. It can be in the twelfth house as long as it's with one or two degrees of the ascendant. If the Rising Planet is within a degree of the ascendant, it can be almost as important and the individual's Sun sign.

Any planet in the first house is accidentally dignified and adds additional emphasis to the planet. For example, consider this loaded first house.

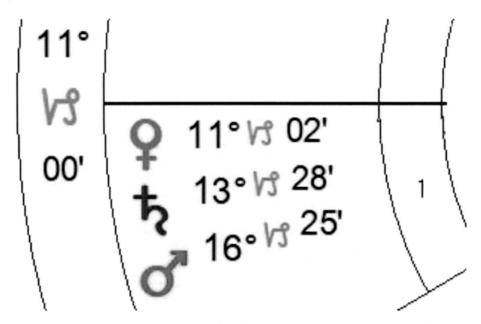

The ascendant is Capricorn, and that makes Saturn the chart ruler. However, Venus is within ten minutes or one-tenth of a degree from the ascendant, and she is the Rising Planet.

The Venusian influence softens the harsh character of Mars and Saturn. Venus is associated with creativity and the arts. Therefore, with Venus as the rising planet, you would expect the individual to be creative and have an active imagination.

Planets don't always cast an aspect, but planets can have *aspect by sign*.

Element	Fire ♈ ♌ ♐	Water ♋ ♏ ♓	Air ♊ ♎ ♒	Earth ♉ ♍ ♑
Fire	Trine	Square	Sextile	Square
Water	Square	Trine	Square	Sextile
Air	Sextile	Square	Trine	Square
Earth	Square	Sextile	Square	Trine

There is an exception to this rule. The polar opposites (see below) are separated by 180°, which forms an opposition. Oppositions have compatible elements, but they are still difficult aspects.

Sign	Element		Sign	Element
Aries	Fire		Libra	Air
Taurus	Earth		Scorpio	Water
Gemini	Air	☍	Sagittarius	Fire
Cancer	Water		Capricorn	Earth
Aquarius	Air		Leo	Fire
Virgo	Earth		Pisces	Water

Aspects between the luminaries represent the internal dialogues between the self-consciousness (Sun), subconsciousness (Moon), and the personality (Ascendant). Before we begin interpreting the aspects, lets briefly review the meanings of planets.

Sun

Sense of individuality. Creative energy, radiant inner self (attunement of soul). Essential values. The urge to be and create. The need to be recognized and to express yourself. The source of will, vitality, and personal power. Qualities of leadership and authority. The center and power of self. The person's purpose and direction in life. The Soul. Life-force. Overall strength in life. The core sense of identity. Self-confidence. Important regarding women's relationships with men.

Moon

The subconscious. Mom and early childhood life. Unconscious reactive habit patterns. Primary emotional needs. Instinctive behaviors that we adopt to get love. Survival instincts. The familiar and comforting. Emotional style. How we satisfy ourselves. Attachment and dependency. Happiness and addictions. Ego-investment and defensiveness. How basic needs are met. Relations with women in general. The Mother Goddess archetype. A woman's maternal style. Reactions. Feeling-instinct responses. Adaptation to life experiences. Providing oneself with nourishment, protection, and assistance. Affection. Touching. Closeness. Capacity to trust. Ability to connect and be intimate. Food. Psychological patterns that arise during infancy. Bodily health.

Ascendant

Our approach to life. Individuality. The personality. Ego. Our behavior. The way we act—the mask or persona we use to shield ourselves from the world. Our expression conditioned by the need for recognition. What we show the world.

For most people, the expression of self is shaped by our relations with family members. As children, our individual expression gets modified and conditioned by our need for recognition, particularly from our mothers and fathers.

Methods of Interpretation

On one level, the Sun, Moon, and Ascendant are symbolic of our fathers (Sun), mothers (Moon), and how our parents shaped our expression of self (Ascendant). Planets are considered *externally* manifested forces embodied by our environment. However, planets are also symbolic of *internal* forces that are a part of us. Keep this in mind when you are interpreting your chart.

The Sun-Moon Relationship

Now it is your turn to interpret your own Sun-Moon relationship. First answer the following questions:

The Sun is _____ (sign and degree)

The Moon is _____ (sign and degree)

Are your Sun and Moon in naturally harmonious or inharmonious signs?

Are they in polar opposite signs?

3. What aspect (conjunction, sextile, etc.), if any, do the Sun and Moon make?

Orb?

How do the Sun and Moon in your chart relate?

The Sun-Ascendant Relationships

The Sun-Ascendant relationship symbolizes how the power of the Sun is expressed through the personality, or how our environment shapes the expression of the qualities of the Sun.

The Sun is _____ (sign and degree)

The Ascendant is _____ (sign and degree)

Are your Sun and Ascendant in naturally harmonious or inharmonious signs?

Are they in polar opposite signs?

What aspect (conjunction, sextile, etc.), if any, do the Sun and Ascendant make?

Orb?

How do the Sun and Ascendant?

Moon-Ascendant Relationships

The Moon-Ascendant relationship symbolizes how the instinctive emotional nature of the Moon is expressed through the individual.

The Moon is _____ (sign and degree)

The Ascendant is _____ (sign and degree)

Are your Moon and Ascendant in naturally harmonious or inharmonious signs?

Are they in polar opposite signs?

What aspect (conjunction, sextile, etc.), if any, do the Sun and Ascendant make?

Orb?

How do your Moon and Ascendant relate?

Chapter 14

Essential Dignities of the Planets

Essential dignity evaluates the strength of a planet. Planets with essential dignity show more positive effects are better integrated into the personality and function more freely in their domains.

There are five essential dignities. Renaissance and medieval astrologers assigned a weighted score.

	Essential Dignity	Score
1	Rulership	+5
2	Exaltation	+4
3	Triplicity	+3
4	Term	+2
5	Face	+1

There are three essential debilities. They are:

	Debility	Score
1	Determent	-5
2	Fall	-4
3	Peregrine	-3

The *essential dignity* judges the planet on by sign and degree.

Accidental dignity judges a planet based on its house placement and aspects to other planets — more on accidental dignities in the next chapter.

Domicile, Rulership or Natural Sign (+5)

Each planet (except the Sun and Moon) has two signs to call home in the zodiac. One is a Day sign and the other is a Night Sign. Notice the Day or Diurnal signs contain the elements *Fire* and *Air*. The Night or Nocturnal signs contain *Water* and *Earth*.

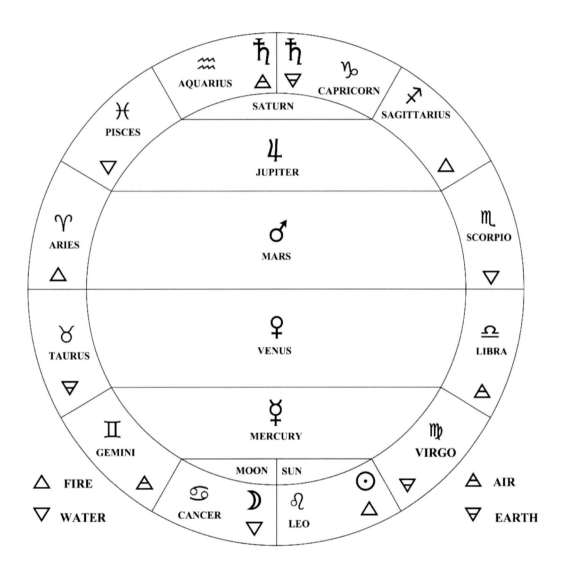

Planet		Sect			
		Day Sign Ruler		Night Sign Ruler	
Sun	☉	Leo	♌		
Moon	☽			Cancer	♋
Mercury	☿	Gemini	♊	Virgo	♍
Venus	♀	Libra	♎	Taurus	♉
Mars	♂	Aries	♈	Scorpio	♏
Jupiter	♃	Sagittarius	♐	Pisces	♓
Saturn	♄	Aquarius	♒	Capricorn	♑

A planet in its sign is like a king on a throne - a sovereign in their kingdom. Planets in Rulership have their resources at hand to execute their desires and provide protection.

"A planet in rulership is in a position of strength. The rulership of a sign denotes a planetary force where you are in control, master of your ship, you initiate what happens. You do what you want. What you end up being, doing, whatever, is not because of external pressure on you, but because you choose it." – Lehman, *Essential Dignities*.

Ezra's Introduction to astrology he has this say about the two malefics, Saturn and Mars.

"Every planet, whether benefic or malefic, always signifies good fortune if it is in its house (the sign of rulership) or the house of its exaltation." p. 219.

For the rest of the book, I use Magnus Carlson's birth chart as an example. His natal horoscope has many interesting characteristics that illustrate essential and accidental dignities.

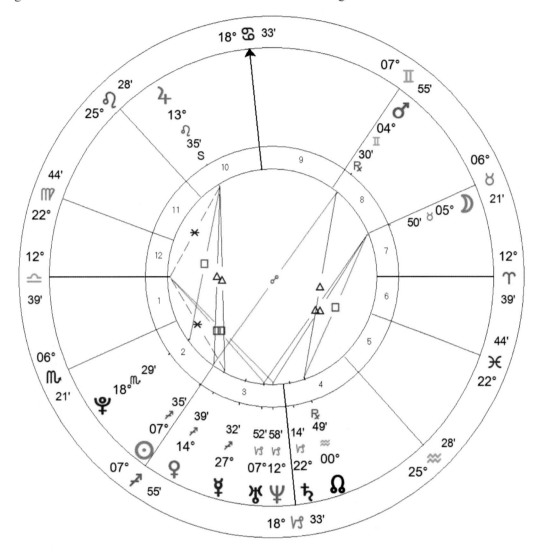

In Magnus Carlson's chart, Saturn rules Capricorn. It is in the fourth house and the natural home of Cancer and the mother. Saturn in the fourth house suggests that the mother was the disciplinarian in the home. And not in a bad way because although Saturn is malefic, she's in rulership.

One of my teachers said that a dignified malefic is like a bad guy in a good mood. He'll help you, but grumble and make you work for it.

Detriment (-5)

A planet in detriment is not comfortable in that sign and is forced to express tendencies opposite to its nature. The planet is weak or has difficulty expressing itself. Planets in detriment are in an unsympathetic environment and can act competitively. They can be nervous and unsure of themselves. Planets in detriment must learn to function in a stressful and unfriendly situation.

Detriment Mercury in Sagittarius

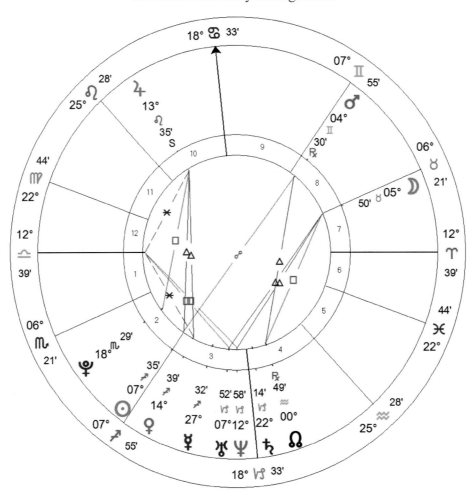

From another point of view, planets in Detriment are powerful. Magnus Carlson is World Chess Champion in classical, rapid, and blitz. His peak rating is 2882, the highest in history. His Mercury is in its Detriment in Sagittarius, but that didn't stop him from playing ten simultaneous chess games blindfolded. Fire signs like Sagittarius are excellent visualizers.

By rearranging the signs, it's easier to see the pattern of Rulership and Detriment.

Sign	Rulership	Detriment	Sign	Rulership	Detriment
♈	♂	♀	♉	♀	♂
♎	♀	♂	♏	♂	♀
♊	☿	♃	♍	☿	♃
♐	♃	☿	♓	♃	☿
♋	☽	♄	♌	☉	♄
♑	♄	☽	♒	♄	☉

Planets in rulership or detriment are powerful. In rulership, the power is easy to direct towards chosen goals. In detriment, you have the power, but you don't know what to do. Like the song by Howard Jones, *You're the fastest runner, but you're not allowed to win.* These are some of the difficulties of planets in detriment. They can be overcome, but only if you work with the planet.

Exaltation (+4)

Planets in rulership are powerful and free to act, but they do not always manifest their best qualities. Mars is an innately harsh, sometimes cruel ruler, so given free rein in Aries and Scorpio, he is likely to show his excesses.

A planet in rulership is king or queen of its domain. A planet in exaltation is like an honored guest in a noble's home. The planet is treated with great respect. However, it doesn't get to do what it wants.

Mars in Aries (cardinal fire) hates limitations and is easily irritated by the indecision of others. His motto is, "Let's do something, even if it's wrong."

Mars in Capricorn is exalted in a cardinal earth sign. As an honored guest in the home of Saturn, Mars learns discipline and planning. His energy is directed into constructive, focused, and durable aims. Mars becomes responsible rather than wanton or capricious. Mars hates rules and limitations, but the lessons learned channels his energy into useful pursuits.

Planets in exaltation are strong, more refined, and may confer a sense of purpose, which is expressed by the house placement and aspects. Planets in exaltation are respected, honored, and when they speak, the other planets listen.

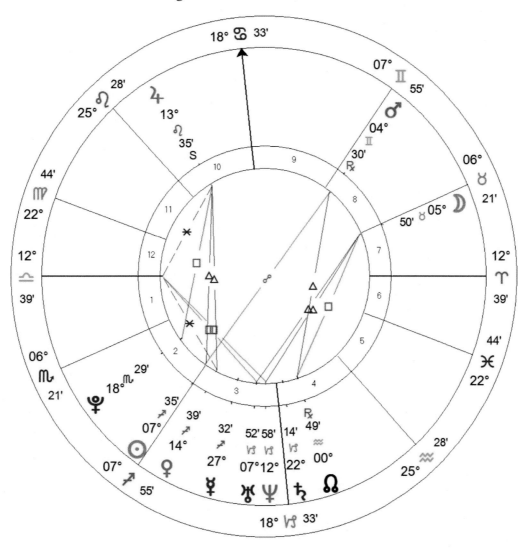

Magnus Carlson – Moon in Taurus

Two planets rule the mind. Mercury is thought, and the Moon is Memory. Notice the Magnus's Moon is *Exalted* in Taurus. Magnus was born at night with the Moon above the horizon. Recall from the chapter on sect - the Moon is *Hayz*.

Hayz of Night Planets in a Night Chart						
	Planets above the Horizon in either of these signs					
☽ + ♀	♉	♋	♍	♏	♑	♓

Also, by Night, the Moon is dignified by *Triplicity* (see below). Needless to say, Magnus Carlson has an excellent Moon and memory.

Fall (-4)

A planet in the sign opposite the sign of its Exaltation is in its Fall. In its Fall, a planet loses strength and influence. They are not respected and can act out to get attention. Psychologically, it can manifest as a poor self-image.

For example, Mars in Capricorn is good at getting things done. The opposite of Capricorn is Cancer. In Cancer, Mars can be moody and passive-aggressive. Mars resists change and avoids confrontations. In Cancer, Mars needs to feel secure before he acts. Therefore, he is slow to take action. However, Mars in Cancer is respectful of other people's feelings, and so he has more friends than Mars in Capricorn or Aries.

Like Rulership, the Exaltations of the plants from a pattern. Notice that no planets are Exalted or Fall in Gemini, Sagittarius, Leo, and Aquarius. However, the North Node is exalted in Gemini and the South in Sagittarius.

Sign	Exalt	Fall		Sign	Exalt	Fall
♈	☉	♄		♉	☽	
♎	♄	☉		♏		☽
♊	NN	SN		♍	☿	♀
♐	SN	NN		♓	♀	☿
♋	♃	♂		♌		
♑	♂	♃		♒		

In Lee Lehman's book, Essential Dignities, he states:

"The point with either a planet in detriment or fall is that the native must put out some effort to circumvent the difficulty. If enough effort is made, *the difficulty can become an asset.* However, it remains for the native to choose to put out that effort. With no effort, the detriments and falls show areas of life which are dysfunctional, or at least, not optimum. As we need reminding occasionally, the polar opposite of positive strength is not weakness, but negative strength." p. 165.

Is Mercury Exalted in Aquarius?

I get asked this question a lot, is Mercury Exalted in Aquarius? To answer this question precisely, No, Yes, and Maybe.

No

No, the ancient astrologer's system of essential dignities shows Mercury is exalted and in rulership in Virgo – end of the story.

Yes

However, Porphyry, in his commentary on the *Tetrabiblios of Ptolemy*, says day planets, the Sun, Jupiter, and Saturn, have their Exaltation in signs to which they are in trine. Nocturnal or night planets the Moon, Venus, and Mars, have their exaltations in signs to which they are sextile. The one planet of mixed-sect, Mercury, has his rulership and exaltation in Virgo.

Day Planets	Rulership	Aspect	Exaltation
Sun	Leo – fix Fire		Aries – cardinal Fire
Jupiter	Pisces – mutable Water	Trine	Cancer – cardinal Water
Saturn	Aquarius – fixed Air		Libra – cardinal Air

Mercury rules Gemini, which is a Day sign. If we consider Mercury a Day planet, we have this table.

	Rulership	Aspect	Exaltation
Mercury	Gemini – mutable Air	Trine	Aquarius – fixed Air

Therefore, there is evidence to suggest that Mercury is exalted in Aquarius.

Maybe

Without passion or agenda, Aquarius is interested in the facts. Therefore, Mercury in Aquarius (and fixed signs in general) is good at research and discovering the truth. However, we are still in the age of Pisces, where ideology trumps facts. For all the lip service given to celebrating diversity, people don't like it when you disagree with them. If you're going to speak the truth, then watch your back.

I am sending you out like sheep among wolves. Therefore be as shrewd as snakes and as innocent as doves. – Matthew 10:16.

Triplicity (+3)

The third essential dignity is Triplicity. It is dependent on the element and sect (Day or Night).

Dignity by Triplicity						
Element	Signs			Day	Night	Participating or Mixed Triplicity
Fire	♈	♌	♐	☉	♃	♄
Earth	♉	♍	♑	♀	☽	♂
Air	♊	♎	♒	♄	☿	♃
Water	♋	♏	♓	♂[1] (♀)	♂	☽

[1] The ancient system has Venus dignified by day in Water signs. The Medieval and Renaissance astrologers switched it to Mars. From experience, Venus is well placed in the water sign Cancer. Water is life, and Venus, the goddess of Love, was born from sea foam. She likes water.

In Ezra's *Introductions to Astrology*, he considers a day planet at night still dignified, but to a lesser extent. In his description of Aries:

"The lords of the triplicity by day are Sun and then Jupiter, and by night Jupiter and then the Sun; Saturn is their partner by day and by night." – p. 63.

Anthony Louis in his astrology blog, Triplicity: The Third Essential Dignity states,

"Dignity is often likened to the type of respect accorded to royalty or important personages. The Pope has dignity by domicile in Vatican City. He is the absolute ruler and final arbiter. His authority is not questioned. When the Pope travels to a Catholic country, like Mexico, he is exalted and treated like an honored guest. He generally gets what he wants, but he must abide by the laws of the Mexican government. When the Pope (Joe Ratzinger) dresses in civilian clothes and visits his family in Germany, he has dignity by triplicity in the homes of his extended family. He is well treated by his extended family, but they are more likely to call him 'Joe' rather than 'Your Holiness.'"

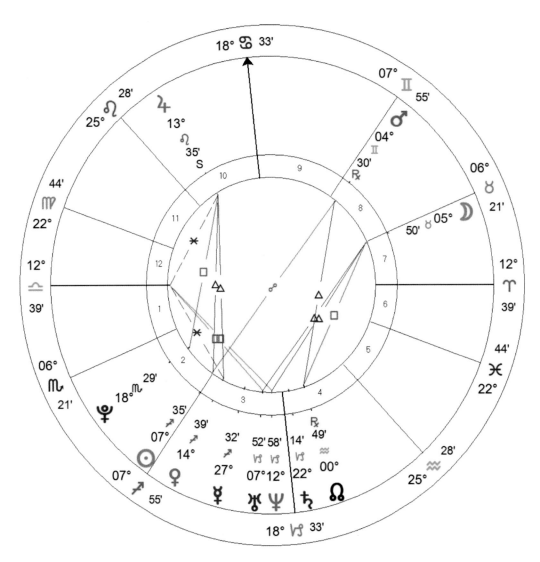

Jupiter, the greater fortune, is dignified by Triplicity in fire signs by Night. In the tenth house, Jupiter bestows his fortune and luck to Magnus's career. Notice the "S" next to Jupiter. It means *Stationary*. More on that in the next chapter on accidental dignities.

Using the Triplicity Lords to Judge a House

One way to determine the strength of a house is to look at the three triplicity lords that rule a house cusp.

The third house is associated with the mind. Magnus' third house cusp is Sagittarius. The triplicity lords of fire signs are Sun by day, Jupiter by night, and Saturn by day and night.

In Magnus' chart, the Sun in Sagittarius is dignified by Triplicity and conjunct the third house cusp by less than a degree. Jupiter is dignified by Triplicity in Leo and casting a trine to the Sun. Jupiter and the Sun are in mutual reception by Rulership, which is discussed in a later chapter.

The mixed Triplicity ruler, Saturn, is in Rulership and conjunct the fourth house cusp.

Even though Mercury in Sagittarius is in its Detriment, the third house triplicity lords are in excellent condition. According to the internet, Magnus Carlson's IQ is 190.

Terms (+2)

The terms are unequal divisions of each sign, which are assigned planetary sub-rulers. These are similar to the decans or Faces, except that there are five subdivisions in each sign instead of three.

The Sun and Moon do not have terms assigned to them. Each of the remaining five planets has one term in each sign. In general (but not always), the first term of each sign is given to the planet ruling or exalted in that sign. Terms at the end of each sign are given to the malefic planets, Mars and Saturn. That why some astrological texts assign bad things to the last degree of a sign.

Planets in their terms are like a competent craftsman. Term is not the master craftsman of Triplicity. But they are skilled enough to be called a journeyman, reliable but not outstanding.

Terms are also called bounds. Terms or bounds limit how a planet expresses itself.

From the table below, Jupiter is in Mars Term. Mars is the Term or Bound Ruler. Even though Jupiter rules Sagittarius, in under Mars' Terms, so he's kind of grumpy. Jupiter is still powerful and does what he wants in rulership. However, his expression is more Mars-like.

Also, when interpretation your chart, look at the Term or Bound ruler of your ascendant and Midheaven. These two Bound Rulers will color how you express yourself.

Sign	TERMS				
♈	♃ 0 – 5°59	♀ 6 – 13°59	☿ 14 – 20°59	♂ 21 -25°59	♄ 26 – 29°59
♉	♀ 0 – 7°59	☿ 8 – 14°59	♃ 15 - 21°59	♄ 22 - 25°59	♂ 26 - 29°59
♊	☿ 0 - 6°59	♃ 7 - 13°59	♀ 14 - 20°59	♄ 21 - 24°59	♂ 25 - 29°59
♋	♂ 0 - 5°59	♃ 6 - 12°59	☿ 13 - 19°59	♀ 20 - 26°59	♄ 27 - 29°59
♌	♄ 0 - 5°59	☿ 6 - 12°59	♀ 13 - 18°59	♃ 19 - 24°59	♂ 25 - 29°59
♍	☿ 0 - 6°59	♀ 7 - 12°59	♃ 13 - 17°59	♄ 18 - 23°59	♂ 24 - 29°59
♎	♄ 0 - 5°59	♀ 6 - 10°59	♃ 11 - 18°59	☿ 19 - 23°59	♂ 24 - 29°59
♏	♂ 0 - 5°59	♃ 6 - 13°59	♀ 14 - 20°59	☿ 21 - 26°59	♄ 27 - 29°59
♐	♃ 0 - 7°59	♀ 8 - 13°59	☿ 14 - 18°59	♄ 19 - 24°59	♂ 25 - 29°59
♑	♀ 0 - 5°59	☿ 6 - 11°59	♃ 12 - 18°59	♂ 19 - 24°59	♄ 25 - 29°59
♒	♄ 0 - 5°59	☿ 6 - 11°59	♀ 12 - 19°59	♃ 20 - 24°59	♂ 25 - 29°59
♓	♀ 0 - 7°59	♃ 8 - 13°59	☿ 14 - 19°59	♂ 20 - 25°59	♄ 26 - 29°59

If a planet is 0 degrees and 1 minute (0°01'), it's in the 1st degree of the sign.

If a planet is 12 degrees and 1 minute (12°01'), it's the 13th degree of the sign.

If a planet is 29 degrees and fifty-nine minutes (29°59'), it's in the 30th degree of a sign.

Faces (+1)

The weakest essential dignity is Face. Faces are also called "decans." Each sign has three Faces or decans of 10 degrees, which is assigned to a planetary ruler.

Faces are barely considered dignities by the medieval and ancient writers. A planet in its face indicates that the individual will have some concern or anxiety about the departments of life denoted by the planet. The planet is highlighted, but it's unclear whether this emphasis is good or bad. To decide, look at the overall dignity of the planet. Otherwise, ill-dignified planets in their faces will indicate some insecurity or anxiety. Well-dignified planets will be more productive.

The faces begin with the first degree of Aries and are assigned a planetary ruler in the Chaldean order. The sequence begins with Mars in the first face of Aries, then proceeds to the Sun, Venus, Mercury, the Moon, Saturn, Jupiter, and back to Mars.

Sign		FACES		
		1	2	3
♈		♂	☉	♀
♉		☿	☽	♄
♊		♃	♂	☉
♋		♀	☿	☽
♌		♄	♃	♂
♍		☉	♀	☿
♎		☽	♄	♃
♏		♂	☉	♀
♐		☿	☽	♄
♑		♃	♂	☉
♒		♀	☿	☽
♓		♄	♃	♂

The Terms and the Faces of the Ascendant and Mid-heaven modify how we express ourselves.

Abraham Ibn Ezra has this to say about planetary dignities.

1. The seven planets give testimonies from their position in the orb. A planet in its house [*Rulership*] resembles a man in his house.

2. A planet in the house of its *exaltation* is like a man at the pinnacle of his rank.

3. A planet in its *term* is like a man on his seat.

4. A planet in the house of its *triplicity* is like a man with his kin.

5. A planet in its *decan* is like a man with his ornaments and garments.

9. A planet in the house of its *detriment* is like a man in conflict with himself.

Homework

Determine the essential dignities of your planets and fill out the table.

If you have a day chart and one of your night planets is in Triplicity, make a note of it. For a night chart with one of your day planets is in Triplicity, note that also.

Planet		Ruler/Det	Exalt/Fall	Triplicity	Term	Face
Sun	☉					
Moon	☽					
Mercury	☿					
Venus	♀					
Mars	♂					
Jupiter	♃					
Saturn	♄					

	Term	Face
Ascendant		
Midheaven		

Chapter 15

Peregrine

A *peregrine* planet has no essential dignity. It is from Latin term meaning foreigner. In old English, to peregrinate, means to wander far from home. It is like a traveler in a foreign country who doesn't know the language and has no social connections. Therefore, peregrine planets have little control over their environment.

For example, a skilled fisherman moves to a desert. In his new location, his knowledge and skills are meaningless. Ezra, in his Introductions to Astrology, says a peregrine *planet in a place where it has no dignity is like a man who is not in his country.*

However, over time peregrine planets get used to working in unusual situations. They learn to live by their wits and have good situational awareness. Peregrine planets can be shrewd, clever and don't operate under the same rules as non-peregrine planets.

When judging a peregrine planet, look to the planet that rules the sign. For example, in Magnus Carlson's chart, Venus is peregrine in Sagittarius.

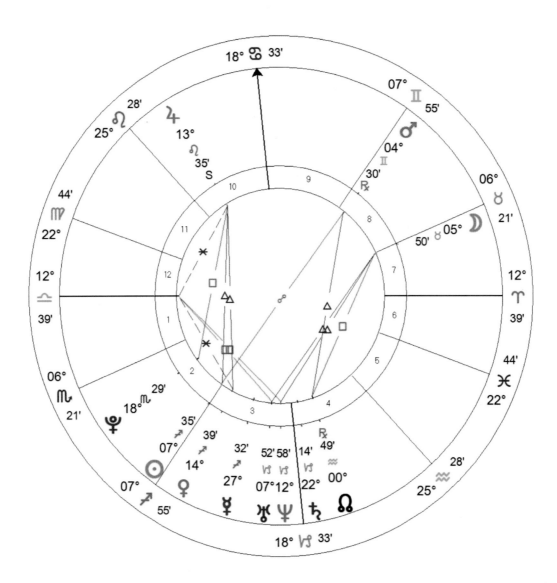

Venus in Sagittarius is fun-loving and likes her freedom. She doesn't want to be tied down. Sagittarius is ruled by Jupiter that is dignified by Triplicity (+3), Term (+2), and stationary direct. Also, Jupiter cast a trine with a tight orb to Venus. Therefore, even though Venus is peregrine, Venus is supported by a well dignified Jupiter.

ARIES ♈					
	Ruler/Det	Exalt/Fall	Triplicity	Term	Face
☉		Exalt	Y		2nd
☽	Peregrine				
☿	Peregrine			14-20	
♀	Detriment		N	6-13	3rd
♂	Ruler		N	21-25	1st
♃			Y	0-5	
♄		Fall	Y	26-29	

The Moon is peregrine for all of Aries. Moon in fire signs has a quick temper.

Mercury is peregrine except for his term. He can be hasty in his decisions but is good at visualizing.

TAURUS ♉					
	Ruler/Det	Exalt/Fall	Triplicity	Term	Face
☉	Peregrine				
☽		Exalt	Y	None	2nd
☿			N	8-14	1st
♀	Ruler		Y	0-7	
♂	Detriment		Y	26-29	
♃	Peregrine			15-21	
♄	Peregrine			22-25	3rd

The Sun is peregrine for all of Taurus. In practice, the Sun in Taurus is dependable and friendly, but his sensual nature tends towards excesses.

Mercury is peregrine except for her term and 1st Decan or Face. Mercury in Taurus has a practical and systematic mind but doesn't make quick decisions.

Jupiter is peregrine except for his term. In Earth signs, Jupiter has trouble giving.

Saturn is peregrine except for his term and face. Saturn in Taurus is good at long term planning.

GEMINI ♊					
	Ruler/Det	Exalt/Fall	Triplicity	Term	Face
☉			N	None	3rd
☽	Peregrine				
☿	Ruler		Y	0-6	
♀		Peregrine		14-20	
♂		Peregrine		25-29	2nd
♃	Detriment		Y	7-13	1st
♄			Y	21-24	

Sun is Peregrine except for the 3rd Face.

The Moon is peregrine for all of Gemini. In practice, she's good at commutating her feelings.

Venus is peregrine except for her term. In Gemini, Venus has trouble deciding on what she wants – fickle.

Mars is peregrine except for his term and face. Mars is quickly bored with routine and needs distractions to stay focused. He prefers outdoor exercise with friends.

CANCER ♋					
	Ruler/Det	Exalt/Fall	Triplicity	Term	Face
☉	Peregrine				
☽	Ruler		Y		3rd
☿	Peregrine			13-19	2nd
♀			Y	20-26	1st
♂		Fall	Y	0-5	
♃		Exalt	N	7-12	
♄	Detriment		N	27-29	

The Sun is peregrine for all of Cancer. The sun's natural fire is dampened in Water signs.

Mercury is peregrine except for her term and face. Cancer the Crab, Scorpio the Scorpion and Pisces the fish do not have mouths and cannot speak. They are considered mute signs. In water signs, Mercury has difficulty expressing herself.

LEO ♌					
	Ruler/Det	Exalt/Fall	Triplicity	Term	Face
☉	Ruler		Y		
☽	Peregrine				
☿	Peregrine			6-12	
♀	Peregrine			13-18	
♂	Peregrine			19-24	3rd
♃			Y	25-29	2nd
♄	Detriment		Y	0-5	1st

The Moon is peregrine for all of Leo. Moon in fire signs has a quick temper.

Mercury is peregrine except for his term. In Leo, Mercury can have an arrogant communication style, but he can speak and write with heart.

Venus is peregrine except for her term. Venus in fire signs is not so good for relationships but excellent for creativity.

Mars is peregrine except for his term and 3rd Decan. Mars likes fire signs, but he has a temper.

VIRGO ♍					
	Ruler/Det	Exalt/Fall	Triplicity	Term	Face
☉	Peregrine				1st
☽			Y		
☿	Ruler	Exalt	N	0-6	3rd
♀		Fall	Y	7-12	2nd
♂			Y	24-29	
♃	Detriment		N	13-17	
♄	Peregrine			18-23	

Sun is peregrine except for the 1st face.

Saturn is peregrine expect for his term. In practice, Saturn is a hard worker in Virgo, but fear of criticism and failure can limit his accomplishments.

LIBRA ♎					
	Ruler/Det	Exalt/Fall	Triplicity	Term	Face
☉		Fall	N		
☽	Peregrine				1st
☿			Y	19-23	
♀	Ruler		N	6-10	
♂	Detriment		N	24-29	
♃			Y	11-18	3rd
♄		Exalt	Y	0-5	2nd

Moon is peregrine except for the 1st Face. In Libra, the Moon feels the highs and lows of every emotion.

SCORPIO ♏					
	Ruler/Det	Exalt/Fall	Triplicity	Term	Face
☉	Peregrine				1st
☽		Fall	Y		
☿	Peregrine			21-26	
♀	Detriment		Y	14-20	3rd
♂	Ruler		Y	0-5	2nd
♃			N	6-13	
♄	Peregrine			27-29	

Sun is peregrine except for the 1st face.

Mercury is peregrine except for her term. Scorpio is a mute sign, and here Mercury has difficulty expressing herself.

Jupiter is peregrine except for his term.

Saturn is peregrine expect for his term. In practice, Saturn in Scorpio is secretive, resourceful, and ambitious.

SAGITTARIUS ♐					
	Ruler/Det	Exalt/Fall	Triplicity	Term	Face
☉			Y		
☽	Peregrine				2nd
☿	Detriment			14-18	1st
♀	Peregrine			8-13	
♂	Peregrine			25-29	
♃	Ruler		Y	0-7	
♄			Y	19-24	3rd

Moon is peregrine expect for the 2nd face.

Venus is peregrine except for her term. She is happy and fun-loving in Sagittarius but dislikes restrictions that come with relationships. However, Venus is creative in Fire signs.

Mars is peregrine except for his term. In fire signs, Mars doesn't have much patience. He needs physical exercise and outdoor activity to be happy and healthy.

CAPRICORN ♑					
	Ruler/Det	Exalt/Fall	Triplicity	Term	Face
☉	Peregrine				3rd
☽	Detriment				
☿	Peregrine			6-11	
♀			Y	0-5	
♂		Exalt	Y	19-24	2nd
♃		Fall	N	12-18	1st
♄	Ruler		N	25-29	

The Sun is peregrine except for the 3rd face. In practice, it's not so bad. Natives are reserved but ambitious.

Mercury is peregrine except for her term. In Capricorn, Mercury is focused on practical problems and doesn't like surprises.

AQUARIUS ♒					
	Ruler/Det	Exalt/Fall	Triplicity	Term	Face
☉	Detriment				
☽	Peregrine				3rd
☿			Y	6-19	2nd
♀		Peregrine		12-19	1st
♂		Peregrine		25-29	
♃			Y	20-24	
♄	Ruler		Y	0-5	

Moon is peregrine except for the 3rd face. Natives are good observers, and the fixed quality of Aquarius makes them good friends. They are not overly emotional but sensitive to attacks on their character.

Venus is peregrine except for her term and 1st face. Natives make good friends, but in relationships, they need freedom and independence.

Mars is peregrine except for his term. Natives are not forceful but willful. I like Mars in Aquarius because natives let people be themselves, and they expect others to do the same.

PISCES ♓					
	Ruler/Det	Exalt/Fall	Triplicity	Term	Face
☉			N		
☽			Y		
☿	Detriment	Fall	N	14-19	
♀		Exalt	Y	0-7	
♂			Y	20-25	3rd
♃	Ruler		N	8-13	2nd
♄			N	26-29	1st

Sun is peregrine for all of Pisces. Sun in Pisces is sensitive.

Saturn is peregrine except for his term and 1st face. In Pisces, Saturn tends to procrastinate.

Chapter 16

Accidental Dignities

An accidental dignity occurs when a planet gains strength for any reason other than its zodiacal position (essential dignity). In Book 2 of *Christian Astrology* (Chapter 28, page 178), Lilly lists the dignities in a table. . I've made one change to the table; I give Retrograde motion a -4 rather than a -5.

Accidental Dignities			Accidental Debilities	
In the 1st & 10th House	+5		In the 12th House	-5
7th, 4th, and 11th House	+4		8th and 6th House	-2
2nd and 5th House	+3			
9th	+2			
3rd	+1			
Swift in Motion	+2		Slow in Motion	-2
Direct in motion	+4		Retrograde	-4
♂, ♃, ♄ – Oriental	+2		♂, ♃, ♄ – Occidental	-2
☽, ☿, ♀ – Occidental	+2		☿, ♀ – Oriental	-2
☽ increasing	+2		☽ decreasing	-2
Free from combust & ☉ Beams	+5		Combust the Sun	-5
			Under the ☉ Beams	-4
Cazimi	+5			
Partile ☌ with ♃, or ♀	+5		Partile ☌, with ♂ or ♄	-5
Partile △ with ♃ or ♀	+4		Partile ☍ with ♂ or ♄	-4
Partile ✶ with ♃ or ♀	+3		Partile □ with ♂ or ♄	-3
Partile ☌ with ☊	+4		Partile ☌ with ☋	-4
			Besieged by ♂ and ♄	-5
Conjunct Regulus	+6		Conjunct Algol	-5
Conjunct Spica	+5			

Accidental Fortitudes and Disabilities by House Placement

The first section of Accidental Dignities describes the strength a planet gains when placed in one of the twelve Houses.

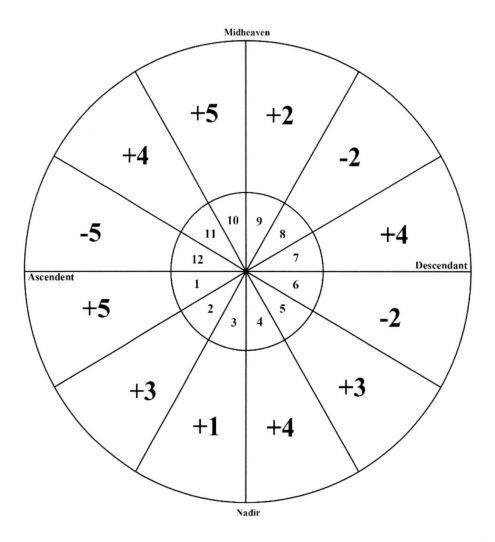

Planets on the angles (1st, 4th, 7th and 10th houses) are very well placed.

Succedent houses are ruled by fixed signs using the natural chart system. Except for the 8th house ruled by Scorpio, succedent houses are favorable.

Cadent houses are ruled by mutable signs and are unfavorable except for the 3rd and ninth houses.

Direct and Retrograde

Retrograde motion is when a planet appears, when observed from Earth, to reverse direction. The Symbol used for retrograde motion is ℞.

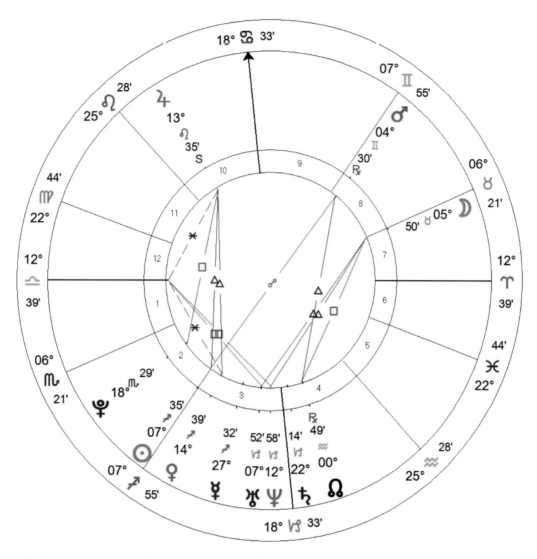

In Magnus Carlson's chart, Mars is retrograde, which is a -4 score. Notice that Mars is within four degrees of the 9th House cusp, so Mars is considered to be in 9th House which is +2.

Mars is peregrine in Gemini except for his term and first face or decan. Carlson's Mars is in the first decan (ten degrees) and gains a +1.

Mars is retrograde. That means its apparent motion in the sky is backward. Generally speaking, retrograde motion means we end up doing something twice because an important detail was left out. Retrograde planets can be too hasty or slow. In practice, I find that retrograde is a minor disability that can be overcome.

In a birth chart, a retrograde Mars, the energy is directed inward. The energy is felt more strongly. This is usually expressed as being shy or awkward when we're young. With Mars in Gemini, I expect Magnus was fidgety during his youth. I expect he enjoys sports that require manual dexterity (Gemini).

Ezra has this to say about retrograde. *A planet that is about to be retrograde is like a panicked man who is afraid of misfortunes that may befall him. A retrograde planet is like a wayward and defiant man.*

Slow, Fast, and Stationary Motions

Swift in Motion	+2		Slow in Motion	-2

The planets revolved around the Sun, but we observe their motions from the earth. Depending on where the planets are in their orbit, their speed changes. A fast Motion is dignity or fortitude, and slow-motion is a disability.

The average daily speeds traveled by the planets are,

Planet		Daily Distance	Comments
Sun	☉	0° 59'	59 minutes
Moon	☽	13° 10' 36"	13 degrees, 10 minutes, 36 seconds
Mercury	☿	1° 23'	1 degree, 23 minutes
Venus	♀	1° 12'	1 degree, 12 minutes
Mars	♂	0° 31'	0 degrees, 31 minutes
Jupiter	♃	0° 05'	5 minutes
Saturn	♄	0° 02'	2 minutes
Uranus	♅	0° 0' 42"	0 degrees, 0 minutes, 42 seconds
Neptune	♆	0° 0' 24"	24 seconds
Pluto	♇	0° 0' 15"	15 seconds

In Magnus' chart, Jupiter is **Stationary Direct**. From the ephemeris is a table of Jupiter's positions.

Nov			Dec	
25	13♎33		1	13♎35 Rx
27	13♎34		2	13♎35 Rx
28	13♎35		3	13♎34 Rx
29	13♎35		4	13♎34 Rx
30	13♎35 Rx		5	13♎33 Rx

There are 60 minutes in a degree and 60 seconds a minute. The average speed of Jupiter is 5 minutes or 1/12 of a degree per day. In Magnus's chart, Jupiter very slow because later in the day, it changes direction from Direct to Retrograde.

James Braha, in the *Art and Practice of Ancient Hindu Astrology*, considers a stationary planet the most potent condition a planet can have. He also adds,

"There's nothing terrible about having an ability and not using it, but when a planet is stationary, it usually signifies extreme talent, and if a person has extreme talent and doesn't use it, the result is depression." – pp. 157 - 158.

Therefore, a slow planet is considered a disability, but a stationary planet is very powerful.

Instead of calculation motions, I use a computer program. This table is from Solar Fire.

Magnus Carlson				T Ønsberg, Norway	
Natal Chart				59°N17' 010°E25'	
Nov 30 1990, Fri		Placidus		Geocentric, Tropical	
3:04 am CET -1:00				Mean Node	

Pt	Long.	F/S	Last Stn	Next Stn	Last Stn	Next Stn
☽	05° ♉ 50'08"	Fast	-	-	-	-
☉	07° ♐ 35'57"	Fast	-	-	-	-
☿	27° ♐ 32'54"	Fast	09° ♍ 35'25"	10° ♑ 00'32"	-73 days	+14 days
♀	14° ♐ 39'23"	Fast	20° ♑ 55'15"	07° ♍ 19'25"	-294 days	+244 days
♂	04° ♊ 30'41"	Retro	14° ♊ 33'46"	27° ♉ 45'11"	-40 days	+32 days
♃	13° ♌ 35'45"	Stat	00° ♋ 48'29"	13° ♌ 35'45"	-278 days	+2h 58m
♄	22° ♑ 14'05"	Fast	18° ♑ 42'14"	06° ♒ 50'31"	-67 days	+168 days
♅	07° ♑ 52'56"	Fast	05° ♑ 36'02"	13° ♑ 48'57"	-76 days	+139 days
♆	12° ♑ 58'33"	Fast	11° ♑ 47'51"	16° ♑ 45'54"	-67 days	+139 days
♇	18° ♏ 29'32"	Fast	14° ♏ 58'06"	20° ♏ 22'38"	-127 days	+83 days
☊	00° ♒ 49'25"	Slow	-	-	-	-
As	12° ♎ 39'13"	Slow	-	-	-	-

Occidental and Oriental Planets

♂, ♃, ♄ – Oriental	+2		♂, ♃, ♄ – Occidental	-2
☽, ☿, ♀ – Occidental	+2		☿, ♀ – Oriental	-2

Occident is Latin for the *west,* and original meaning is *falling* or *setting*. Orient is Latin for the *east,* and original meaning is *rising*.

A planet is occidental to the Sun when it rises after the Sun. If you rotate the chart, so the Sun is on the Ascendant, planets below the horizon are occidental. The Moon, Mercury, and Venus are *accidentally dignified* when occidental.

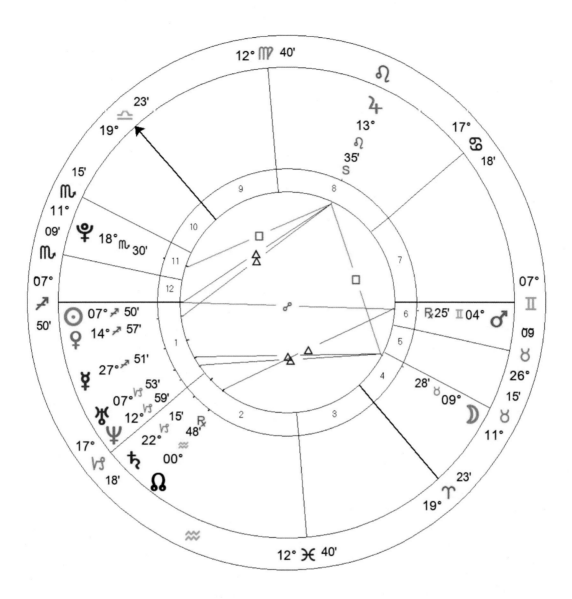

The 8th degree of Gemini to the 8th degree of Sagittarius is occident to the Sun. Venus, Mercury, Uranus, Neptune, Saturn, the Moon, and Mars are occidental. Pluto and Jupiter are Oriental, which means they rise before the Sun.

Therefore, the Moon, Mercury, and Venus gain +2 dignity for being occidental to the Sun. Jupiter gains +2 for being oriental.

Saturn receives a -2 for being occidental. The transpersonal planets Uranus, Neptune, and Pluto, are not part of the accidental dignity system.

Moon Waxing (Increasing) and Waning (decreasing)

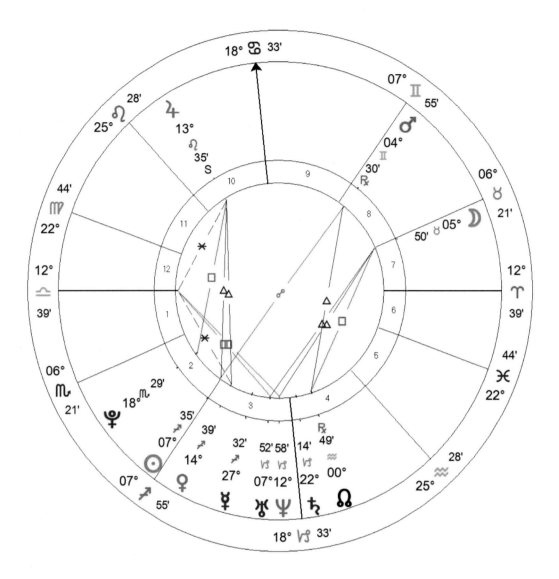

A waxing moon is increasing in light, and this is a +2 fortitude. You can tell a waxing or waning Moon by the relationship between the Sun and Moon. The Sun is in the 8ᵗʰ degree (7♐50') of Sagittarius.

In Magnus' chart, his Moon is the 10ᵗʰ degree of Taurus. Since the Moon moves thirteen degrees a day, in a little more than two days, the Moon will be full in of Gemini (7♊50').

Cazimi, Combust and Under the Sun's Beams

Free from combust	+5		Combust the Sun	-5
& ☉ Beams			Under the ☉ Beams	-4
Cazimi	+5			

Cazimi is a conjunction with an orb of sixteen minutes (0°16') or less to the Sun. Cazimi is considered the heart of the Sun.

The corona of the Sun is so bright that any planet within 8°30' or 8.5 degrees of the Sun, it will not be seen. This is called *combust*.

Modern astrologers consider 17 degrees from the Sun as, *under the sunbeams*. In Ezra's *Introductions to Astrology*, he gives 12 degrees for under the sunbeams.

Venus Combust

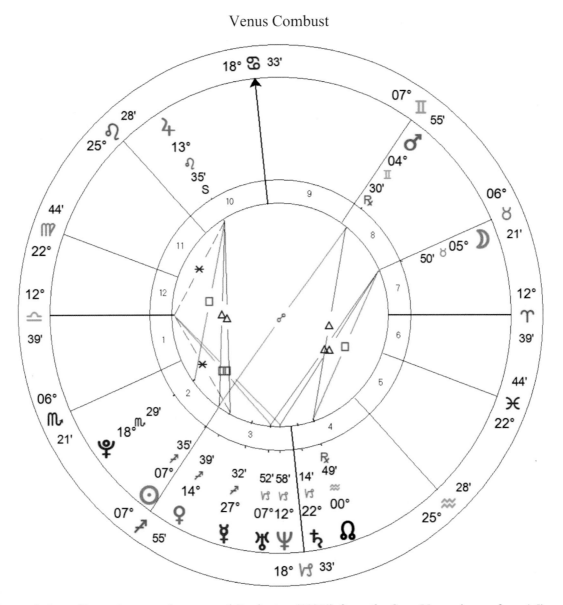

In Magnus' chart, Venus is seven degrees and 7 minutes (7°07') from the Sun. Venus is *combust* (-5).

A combust planet takes a back seat to the Sun. Combust planets have to learn to speak up. They tend to have their thoughts and feelings overlooked and overshadowed by the Sun.

Combust planet in horary astrology, is debilitated. From experience, I'm hesitant to call a combust or planet under the sunbeams debilitated. Like the disabilities peregrine and retrograde, combust can be cover come with effort.

Mercury Combust or Under the Sunbeams

In *Introductions to Astrology* (p. 201), Ezra says, *Mercury, because of its many motions and proximity to the Sun, is always only slightly harmed by the Sun when it is under the ray of the Sun or in the domain of burning [combust].*

Ezra says *A planet under the ray of the Sun is like a man in prison. A planet that is burnt [combust] is like a terminally ill person.*

Chariots

The *Introduction to the Tetrabiblos* states a planet is *in their Chariots* when they are either in Rulership, Exaltation, Triplicity, or Term. When a planet is in its Chariots, it is not harmed by being under the sunbeams. Instead, it adds benefit.

A planet in its chariots is like a manger of a firm being visited by the company's president. The president (the Sun) shines a light on another planet's achievements.

Conjunction to Fixed Stars

According to Lilly, two fixed stars add fortitude, and one gives a disability when they are conjunct a planet.

Regulus, Spica, and Algol are three of the fifteen Behenian stars.

Star	Location	Dignity/disability
Regulus	29 ♌ 50	+6
Spica	23 ♎ 47	+5
Algol	26 ♉ 07	-6

Behenian Fixed Stars

The Behenian fixed stars are 15 stars considered useful for magical applications in medieval astrology. Heinrich Cornelius Agrippa discussed them in his Three Books of Occult Philosophy.

	Name	Constellation	Location	Brightness Rank	Apparent Magnitude
				Behenian Stars	
1	Algol	Perseus	26 ♉ 07	60	2.12
2	Pleiades	Star Cluster M45	29 ♉ 55	[1]	1.6
3	Aldebaran (royal star)	Eye of Taurus	9 ♊ 11	14	0.86
4	Capella	Alhayhoch Goat	21 ♊ 48	6	0.08
5	Sirius, Dog Star		14 ♋ 03	1	-1.46
6	Procyon	Lesser Dog	25 ♋ 45	8	0.34
7	Regulus (royal star)	Heart of Leo the Lion	29 ♌ 47	21	1.4
8	Polaris	Tail of Great Bear		48	1.79
9	Algorab,	Raven	13 ♎ 27		2.96
10	Spica	Virgo	23 ♎ 47	16	0.97
11	Arcturus	Bootes	24 ♎ 11	4	-0.5
12	Alphecca	The Northern Crown	12 ♏ 14		2.23
13	Antares	Heart of Scorpio	9 ♐ 43	15	0.6 – 1.6
14	Vega, The Vulture	Lyre	15 ♑ 16	5	+0.02
15	Deneb Algedi	Tail of Capricorn	5 ♓ 18		2.81

[1] The Pleiades are a cluster of stars.

I check for conjunctions to these fixed stars when reading a chart. I use three degrees for applying conjunction and two degrees for separating conjunction.

Aspects to Benefic and Malefic Planets

Partile Conjunction with ♃, or ♀	+5		Partile Conjunction, with ♂ or ♄	-5
Partile Trine with ♃ or ♀	+4		Partile opposition with ♂ or ♄	-4
Partile Sextile with ♃ or ♀	+3		Partile Square with ♂ or ♄	-3
Partile Conjunction with ☊	+4		Partile Conjunction with ☋	-4
			Besieged by ♂ and ♄	-5

Depending on the author, a partile aspect is either,

1. An aspect with a 0 degrees orb.

2. An aspect with an orb of 1 degree or less.

3. An aspect with an orb of 3 degrees or less.

I use an orb of 3 degrees or less for applying conjunction and two degrees for separating conjunction. Aspects and conjunctions to the two benefices give ease and luck to the houses that the planets reside.

Malefics bring hardship and difficulties to overcome.

In Magnus' chart, Venus is 14°♐39,' and Jupiter is 13°♌35'. Since Venus is the faster planet, this is a separating trine with an orb of four minutes (04') or 1/15 of a degree. Even though his Venus is combust, this is a lovely Venus.

A besieged planet is one that separates from a malefic and applies an aspect to another malefic. Besiegement can occur by aspect or conjunction. It symbolizes a planet trapped on each side by hostile forces.

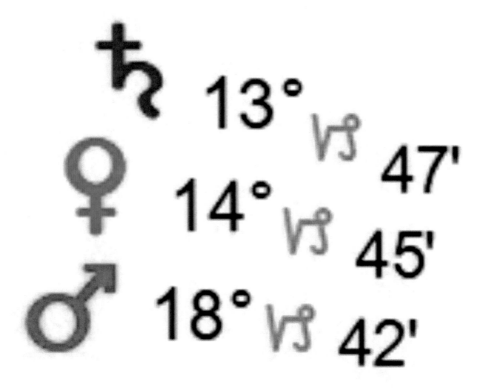

In the diagram above, Venus is besieged by the two malefics. Venus is in a *separating conjunction* to Saturn with an orb of 0 degrees and 58 minutes (0°59'). Also, Venus is in an *applying conjunction* to Mars with an orb of 3 degrees and 57 minutes (3°57'). It is a terrible day for Venus.

In the figure above, the Moon is making a partile separating conjunction to the North Node. The orb is 2 degrees and 0 minutes (2°00').

Chapter 17

Mutual Reception

Planets in Mutual Reception work well together. They gain strength and take on each other's qualities and gather energy from each other. Mutual receptions are hidden strengths. If there is no aspect between the two planets (Sextile, Trine, Square, and Opposition), they still work well together. However, if they are linked by aspect, the connection is stronger. The hard or challenging aspects (square and opposition) are lessened or moderated.

When interpreting Mutual Receptions, you have to consider the planet's essential dignities and disabilities. Mutual reception is when two planets are in each other's signs of Rulership. This reception is the best, but reception by Exaltation and Triplicity are very good. Term and Face Mutual Receptions are the least.

Mutual receptions between planets in Detriment do not help each other that much. Instead, help comes from an outside source. Mars in Taurus (Detriment) married to a Venus in Scorpio (Detriment) needs the help of a couple's counselor to work things out.

Also, there is mixed receptions. Below is a table from Solar Fire. Notice there can be mixed Mutual Receptions between, Rulership-Exaltation, Rulership-Triplicity, Rulership-Term and Rulership-Face.

MUT. RECEPTIONS		
♂	♄	Ruler-Exalt
☽	♀	Ruler-Trip
♂	♄	Ruler-Face
♄	☽	Trip-Term
♄	☽	Trip-Face
♂	♃	Term-Term

The following pages are tabulations of some, but not all, of the Mutual Receptions.

There are dozens of Mutual Receptions between the planets. The most powerful receptions are shown in the two tables.

Planet	Sign		Planet	Sign
☽	♉		♀	♋
♄	♊		☿	♒
♃	♋		♀	♓
♃	♎		♀	♓
♄	♎		♀	♑
☉	♐		♃	♈
☉	♐		♃	♌
♄	♐		♃	♒
☿	♒		♄	♊
☽	♓		♃	♋
♀	♓		♃	♎
♀	♓		♃	♋
♂	♓		♃	♈

Mutual Reception by Planet

The Sun's Mutual Receptions					
☉	♈	♂	♌	☉ ♈ - ♂ ♌	Good
	♉	♀		☉ ♉ - ♀ ♌	
	♊	☿		☉ ♊ - ☿ ♌	
	♋	☽		☉ ♋ - ☽ ♌	
N/A	♌				
☉	♍	☿	♌	☉ ♍ - ☿ ♌	
	♎	♀		☉ ♎ - ♀ ♌	
	♏	♂		☉ ♏ - ♂ ♌	
	♐	♃		☉ ♐ - ♃ ♌	Excellent
	♑	♄		☉ ♑ - ♄ ♌	♄ Detriment
	♒	♄		☉ ♒ - ♄ ♌	Detriment
	♓	♃		☉ ♓ - ♃ ♌	

The Moon's Mutual Receptions					
☽	♈	♂	♋	☽ ♈ - ♂ ♋	
	♉	♀		☽ ♉ - ♀ ♋	Excellent
	♊	☿		☽ ♊ - ☿ ♋	
N/A	♋				
☽	♌	☉	♋	☽ ♌ - ☉ ♋	
	♍	☿		☽ ♍ - ☿ ♋	
	♎	♀		☽ ♎ - ♀ ♋	
	♏	♂		☽ ♑ - ♂ ♋	Fall
	♐	♃		☽ ♐ - ♃ ♋	
	♑	♄		☽ ♑ - ♄ ♋	Detriment
	♒	♄		☽ ♒ - ♄ ♋	♄ Detriment
	♓	♃		☽ ♓ - ♃ ♋	Good

Mercury's Mutual Receptions						
☿	♈		♂	♊ & ♍	☿ ♈ - ♂ ♊ or ♍	
	♉		♀		☿ ♉ - ♀ ♊ or ♍	♀ ♊ Nice
N/A	♊					
☿	♋		☽		☿ ♋ - ☽ ♊ or ♍	
	♌		⊙		☿ ♌ - ⊙ ♊ or ♍	
N/A	♍					
☿	♎		♀	♊ & ♍	☿ ♎ - ♀ ♊ or ♍	
	♏		♂		☿ ♏ - ♂ ♊ or ♍	
	♐		♃		☿ ♍ - ♃ ♊ or ♍	Detriment
	♑		♄		☿ ♑ - ♊ or ♍	
	♒		♄		☿ ♒ - ♄ ♊ or ♍	Excellent
	♓		♃		☿ ♓ - ♃ ♊ or ♍	Detriment

Saturn in Gemini (Triplicity) is in the sign of Mercury's rulership. Mercury in Aquarius (Triplicity) is in the sign of Saturn's rulership. This is a powerful mutual reception that is more powerful if the Saturn and Mercury are aspecting each other.

Venus' Mutual Receptions						
♀	♈		♂	♉ ♎	♀ ♈ - ♂ ♎ or ♉	Detriment
N/A	♉					
♀	♊		☿	♉ & ♎	♀ ♊ - ☿ ♎ or ♉	Nice
	♋		☽		♀ ♋ - ☽ ♎ or ♉	☽ ♉ Excellent
	♌		⊙		♀ ♌ - ⊙ ♎ or ♉	
	♍		☿		♀ ♍ - ☿ ♎ or ♉	
N/A	♎					
♀	♏		♂	♉ & ♎	♀ ♏ - ♂ ♎ or ♉	
	♐		♃		♀ ♐ - ♃ ♎ or ♉	
	♑		♄		♀ ♑ - ♄ ♎ or ♉	♄ ♎ Good
	♒		♄		♀ ♒ - ♄ ♎ or ♉	
	♓		♃		♀ ♓ - ♃ ♎ or ♉	♃ ♎ Excellent

Mars' Mutual Receptions						
N/A	♈					
♂	♉		♀	♈ & ♏	♂ ♉ - ♀ ♈ or ♏	Detriment
	♊		☿		♂ ♊ - ☿ ♈ or ♏	
	♋		☽		♂ ♋ - ☽ ♈ or ♏	Fall
	♌		☉		♂ ♌ - ☉ ♈ or ♏	☉ ♈ Good
	♍		☿		♂ ♍ - ☿ ♈ or ♏	
	♎		♀		♂ ♎ - ♀ ♈ or ♏	Detriment
N/A	♏					
♂	♐		♃		♂ ♐ - ♃ ♈ or ♏	♃ ♈ Nice
	♑		♄		♂ ♑ - ♄ ♈ or ♏	
	♒		♄		♂ ♒ - ♄ ♈ or ♏	
	♓		♃		♂ ♓ - ♃ ♈ or ♏	Good ♃ ♈

Jupiter's Mutual Receptions						
♃	♈		♂	♐ & ♓	♃ ♈ - ♂ ♐ or ♓	Good
	♉		♀		♃ ♉ - ♀ ♐ or ♓	♀ ♓ Good
	♊		☿		♃ ♊ - ☿ ♐ or ♓	Detriment
	♋		☽		♃ ♋ - ☽ ♐ or ♓	☽ ♓ Excellent
	♌		☉		♃ ♌ - ☉ ♐ or ♓	☉ ♐ Excellent
	♍		☿		♃ ♍ - ☿ ♐ or ♓	Detriment
	♎		♀		♃ ♎ - ♀ ♐ or ♓	♀ ♓ Excellent
	♏		♂		♃ ♏ - ♂ ♐ or ♓	
N/A	♐					
♃	♑		♄		♃ ♑ - ♄ ♐ or ♓	
	♒				♃ ♒ - ♄ ♐ or ♓	♄ ♐ Excellent
N/A	♓					

Saturn's Mutual Receptions						
♄	♈	♂	♑ & ♒	♄ ♈ - ♂ ♒ or ♑		
	♉	♀		♄ ♉ - ♀ ♒ or ♑		
	♊	☿		♄ ♊ - ☿ ♒ or ♑	☿ ♒ Excellent	
	♋	☽		♄ ♋ - ☽ ♒ or ♑	Detriment	
	♌	☉		♄ ♌ - ☉ ♒ or ♑	Detriment	
	♍	☿		♄ ♍ - ☿ ♒ or ♑		
	♎	♀		♄ ♎ - ♀ ♒ or ♑	♀ ♑ Good	
	♏	♂		♄ ♏ - ♂ ♒ or ♑		
	♐	♃		♄ ♐ - ♃ ♒ or ♑	♃ ♒ Excellent	
N/A	♑					
N/A	♒					
♄	♓	♃		♄ ♓ - ♃ ♒ or ♑		

Dignity by Sign

Using these tables, I judged the strength of a mutual reception.

♈ - ♉ Dignities					
☉	♈	Exalt	☉	♉	Peregrine
☽		Peregrine	☽		Exalt
☿		Peregrine	☿		Peregrine
♀		Detriment	♀		Detriment
♃		Triplicity	♃		Peregrine
♄		Fall	♄		Peregrine
♅			♅		Fall
♆			♆		
♇			♇		Detriment

The Moon is Peregrine for all of Aries.

Mars is peregrine in Aries except for his term and 3rd Decan.

The Moon in Taurus (Exalted) is in the sign of Venus' rulership. Venus in Cancer (Triplicity) is in the sign of the Moon's rulership. This is a powerful mutual reception that is more powerful if the Moon and Venus are aspecting each other.

The Sun and Saturn are strong in Taurus but tend to be lazy. If the Sun find activities he likes (Venus rulership of Taurus), he's a dependable worker.

Mercury is peregrine except for her term and 1st Decan. Mercury in Taurus has a practical and methodical mind but doesn't make quick decisions.

♊ - ♋						
Dignities						
☉		Peregrine		☉		Peregrine
☽		Peregrine		☿		Peregrine
☿		Peregrine		♀		Triplicity
♂		Peregrine		♂		Fall
♃	♊	Detriment		♃	♋	Exalt
♄		Triplicity		♄		Detriment
♅				♅		
♆				♆		
♇				♇		

The Sun is Peregrine in Gemini except for the 3rd Face.

Venus in Cancer is in Mutual Reception with the Moon in Taurus. This is a powerful mutual reception by Rulership that is more powerful if the Moon and Venus are aspecting each other.

The Sun is Peregrine for all of Cancer.

♌ - ♍ Dignities					
☽		Peregrine	☉		Peregrine
☿		Peregrine	☽		Triplicity
♀		Peregrine	♀		Fall
♂	♌		♂	♍	Triplicity
♃		Triplicity	♃		Detriment
♄		Detriment	♄		
♅		Detriment	♅		Detriment
♆			♆		
♇			♇		

The Moon is Peregrine for all of Leo.

Mars in Leo can be prideful.

The Sun is Peregrine in Virgo except for the 1st Face.

♎ - ♏ Dignities					
☉		Fall	☉		Peregrine
☽		Peregrine	☽		Fall
☿		Triplicity	☿		Peregrine
♂	♎	Detriment	♀	♏	Detriment
♃		Triplicity	♃		Peregrine
♄		Exalt	♄		
♅			♅		Exalt
♆			♆		Detriment
♇			♇		Ruler

The Moon is Peregrine in Libra except for the 1st Face.

The Sun is Peregrine Scorpio except for the 2nd Face.

	♐				♑	
☉		Triplicity		☉		Peregrine
☽		Peregrine		☽		Detriment
☿		Detriment		☿		Peregrine
♀		Peregrine		♀		Triplicity
♂	♐			♂	♑	Exalt
♄		Triplicity		♃		Fall
♅				♅		
♆				♆		
♇				♇		

The Moon is Peregrine in Sagittarius except for the 2nd Face.

Mars in Sagittarius can scatter his energies.

The Sun is Peregrine in Capricorn, except for the 3rd Face.

	♒				♓	
☉		Detriment		☉		Peregrine
☽		Peregrine		☽		Triplicity
☿		Triplicity		☿		Detriment
♀		Peregrine		♀		Exalt
♂	♒	Peregrine		♂	♓	Triplicity
♃		Triplicity		♄		Peregrine
♅		Ruler		♅		
♆				♆		Ruler
♇				♇		

The Moon is Peregrine in Aquarius except for the 3rd Face.

The Sun is Peregrine for all of Pisces.

Chapter 18

Other Planetary Fortitudes

I know the last chapter was a lot of information. I sorry, there's more to go. I tell my students you only need to know enough astrology to read your chart. Then one of my students replied, "That's a lot of astrology."

When reviewing a chart, I go through a mental checklist. Many techniques don't apply every chart, but you have to fill in the tables before you can judge a chart. Astrology programs do the tedious tabulations. Programs provide a lot of information. However, you need to know what is important when reading a natal chart.

Planetary House of Joys

Each planet has a house most suited to their natural expression. It is their *house of joy*.

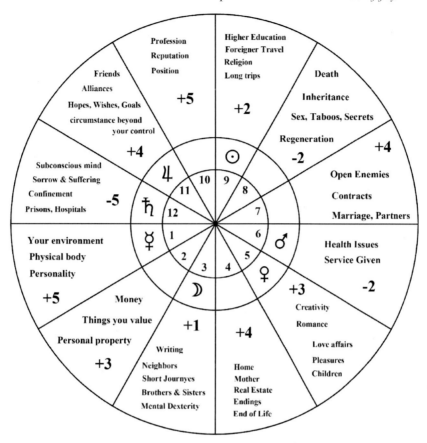

Mercury joys in the first house. Mercury expresses himself naturally through the personality.

The Moon's Joy is in the third house. It is called the House of the Goddess because of the Moon's Joy.

Venus' Joy is in the fifth house. Venus is creative, and in the house of creation, she excels.

Mars' Joy is in the sixth house. Here his energies are put to good use in service. Mars in the sixth does not suffer a -2 disability.

Sun Joy is in the ninth house. The Sun is the symbol of the soul that loves new experiences and the study of holy things.

Jupiter's Joy is in the eleventh house. Jupiter likes nothing better than being surround by friends.

Saturn Joy is in the twelfth house. Saturn prefers to be alone, and sorrow is second nature to him. He is not penalized a -5 for being in his house of joy.

Planetary Dispositor

A dispositor is a planet that rules the sign that another planet is located.

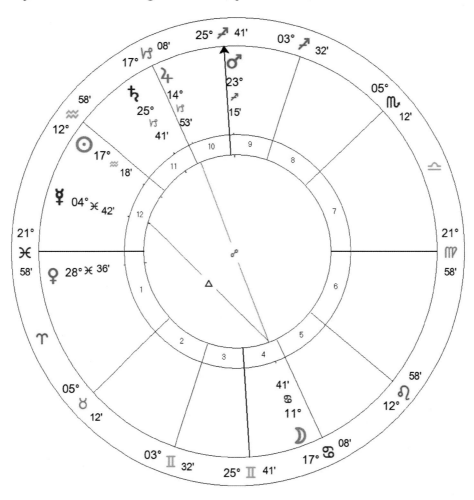

This chart is for 6 February 2020, 8:37 AM.

Mars is in Sagittarius, which is ruled by Jupiter. Jupiter is in Capricorn, which is ruled by Saturn. Saturn rules Capricorn and therefore is the dispositor of both Mars and Jupiter.

Planet		Dispositor			Dispositor	
♂	♐	♃	♑		♄	♑
☉	♒	♄	♑			
☿	♓	♃	♑		♄	♑
♀	♓	♃	♑		♄	♑
♄	♑					
☽	♋					

The dispositor planet exerts control over the planets being disposited because they rely on the dispositor for support. In the chart above, Saturn directly influences all the planets except the Moon in Cancer. The Moon is in her sign of rulership, so no planet tells the Moon what to do.

Final Dispositor

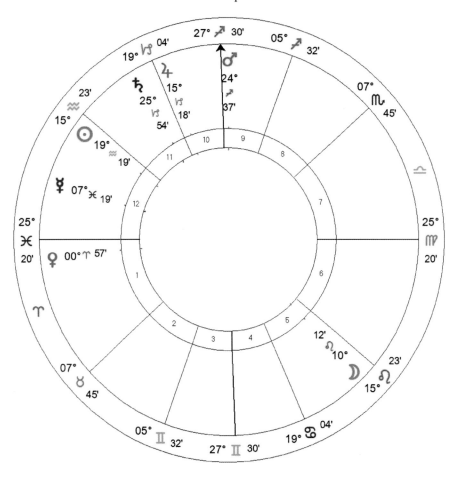

This is a chart for 8 February 2020, 8:37 AM. The Moon is in Leo.

Planet		Dispositor			Final Dispositor	
♂	♐	♃	♑		♄	♑
☉	♒	♄	♑			
☿	♓	♃	♑		♄	♑
♀	♓	♃	♑		♄	♑
♄	♑	Final Dispositor				
☽	♌	☉	♒		♄	♑

In this chart, Saturn is the *final dispositor*. Since he is the only planet in his sign, nobody tells him what to do. Therefore, Saturn influences all other planets in the chart.

In charts where no planets are in their signs of rulership, there is no final dispositor.

Planet-Sign-House

By now, you've looked up your planets by signs and houses either online or purchased Volume One of *The Only Way to Learn Astrology*. There are other good books on astrology, but that was my first astrology textbook and I'm partial to it.

A basic technique is to take the keywords of the planet, sign, and house and form a sentence. I visualize the planets as actors doing things and talking to each other. Jupiter is fat and happy, and Saturn is old and thin. Mars has red hair and broken teeth from his many fights. Venus looks like Michelle Pfeiffer. The starring role of our passion play is the Sun, and the best-supporting actress award goes to the Moon. The planets are the actors, the signs their roles, the houses the scenes.

First, fill out the chart of essential and accidental dignities/disabilities. Use the numerical scores from previous lessons. These tables and tabulations tell whether the two malefics Mars and Saturn are bad guys in a good mood or bad boys in a foul mood. And Venus can be the good girl in *Witches of Eastwick* or the bad girl in *Stardust*.

The blending of these characteristics is both *art* and *science*. The science is the memorization of keywords and facts, and the art is blending them in a meaningful way.

Before you begin, a summary of the house and signs.

House	Attributes
1	Personal identity. The awareness of self. Self-image. The physical body & appearance. Behavior. The personality. Overall attitude (persona).
2	Security. Earned income. Self-worth. Resources. Talent(s) used to make money.
3	The concrete mind. Concepts & language. How we gather information. Writings. Short journeys. Ones thinking, speaking, & writing styles. Siblings & neighbors
4	Security. The home & conditions of home life. Family. How we nurture ourselves. Privacy needs.
5	Pleasure. Fun & games. Speculation. Amusement. Creativity. Casual relationships. Creative self-expression. Children as a means of self-expression. Minor love affairs as amusement.
6	Employment & the employer. Duty. Accidents. Service to others. Maintenance. Illness & health issues.
7	What we attract in a relationship. Our projections & shadow. Dealing with people one to one. Marriage, partnerships, contracts, & open enemies.
8	The breaking of attachments, hence death, changes, transformations, inheritance, growth. Hidden legacies & business. Transformation essential to growth. Sexuality & the death/rebirth process. Values & resources of others. Secret desires, impulses, and instincts. Secrets and taboos.
9	Philosophy. Religion. Long journeys. Matters of law. Higher education. Making sense of "it." Perspective & belief systems. Spiritual orientation.
10	Position. Honor. Authority & status. Recognition. What you are called to do. The office you hold. Public image & career. What needs recognition. How success is defined. The discovery of one's spiritual identity. Standards of competency.
11	Hopes & wishes. Social life. Collective ideas. Social rules & lessons. Friendship criteria. Circle of friends. The groups we are members of. Progressive politics & social reform. Humanitarian ventures & shared ideals.
12	Fate. Obstacles. Confinement. Karma. Hidden enemies. Subconscious states. Losing boundaries. Blindspot. Refuge. Mysticism. Where we undo ourselves (shoot ourselves in the foot). Accumulated resources, both positive & negative.

Planet	Attributes
Asc.	Individuality. The personality. Ego. Our behavior. The way we act. The mask or persona we use to shield ourselves from the world. What we show the world.
☉	Sense of individuality. Creative energy. Need to be recognized & to express self. The source of will, vitality, and personal power. The center & power of self. The person's purpose & direction in life. Life-force. Overall strength in life. Self-confidence.
☽	Unconscious reactive habit patterns. Primary emotional needs. Survival instincts. The familiar and comforting. Emotional style. Attachment and dependency. A woman's maternal style. Reactions. Adaptation to life experiences. The subconscious.
☿	The conscious mind (logical or rational mind). How we communicate, think, and process information. How we solve problems. Intellect. Comprehension and logical processes. The Messenger archetype.
♀	Tastes. Sharing. What we like. Personal love. Romance. Relationship patterns. How we attract intimacy. How beauty is defined. What is pleasing to us. Self-acceptance & worth.
♂	The principles of energy, force, will, desire, and passion. Sexuality. The will to act. Initiative. Physical energy. Force & might. Drive to initiate action. What gets us angry and how we fight. Warrior archetype. Self-defense & aggression. Self-assertion.
♃	Contraction. Limitation. Restriction. Discipline. Sorrow. Hardships. The father and authority issues. Work. Effort. Karma. Form and definition. Where effort, hard work, and responsibility are required to succeed. Commitment. Rules. Responsibility. Stability.
♄	Expansion. Opportunity. Success. Prosperity Growth. Grace. What draws you out and gives optimism. Social laws. Cooperation. Civilization. How I seek to grow and trust in life. One's beliefs. Support. Protection. Generosity. Abundance. Intuition. Religion.
♅	Change. Disruption. Revolution. Instability. Eccentricity. Inventiveness. Autonomy. Originality. Genius. Electrical. Unpredictable events. Sudden crisis. Psyche-shattering events.
♆	Urge to return to harmony and unity. Service & self-sacrifice. Escapism. Psychism. Psychic phenomena. Escapist tendencies. Unconditional love. Martyrdom. High ideals & expectations & therefore disillusionment.
♇	Cleansing. Healing. Taboos. Secrets. Death & rebirth. Deep shock & Spiritual crisis. Area of greatest change. Soul Intent. Obsession & compulsive acts. Sexual/spiritual fusion.

The Sun

My Sun is in _____ (sign and symbol) in the _____ House.

	Dignity	Disability
Ruler		
Detriment		
Exaltation		
Fall		
Triplicity		
Term		
Face		
Peregrine		
House Score		
Haz		
Partile Aspects		
Conjunct Fixed Stars		
House of Joy?		
Dispositor?		
Mutual Reception?		

The Sun's House and Sign attributes that you identify with.

House attributes:

Sign attributes:

Combine the qualities of the Sun, house, and into a phrase or sentence.

The Moon

My Moon is in _____ (sign and symbol) in the _____ House.

	Dignity	Disability
Ruler		
Detriment		
Exaltation		
Fall		
Triplicity		
Term		
Face		
Peregrine		
House Score		
Fast/Slow		
Haz		
Oriental/Occident		
Combust/Beams Cazimi		

Partile Aspects?	
Conjunct Fixed Stars?	
Moon waxing/waning?	
House of Joy?	
Dispositor?	
Mutual Reception?	

The Moon's House and Sign attributes that you identify with.

House attributes:

Sign attributes:

Combine the qualities of the Moon house and sign into a phrase or sentence.

The Ascendant

Remember, the Ascendant is the Cusp of the 1st House.

My Ascendant is in _____ (sign and symbol).

Attributes of the First House cusp and its sign.

1st House attributes:

Sign attributes:

Combine the qualities of the Ascendant in its sign into a phrase or sentence.

Mercury

My Mercury is in _____ (sign and symbol) in the _____ House.

	Dignity	Disability
Ruler		
Detriment		
Exaltation		
Fall		
Triplicity		
Term		
Face		
Peregrine		
House Score		
Fast/Slow		
Retrograde/Direct		
Haz		
Oriental/Occident		
Combust/Beams Cazimi		

Partile Aspects?	
Conjunct Fixed Stars?	
House of Joy?	
Dispositor?	
Mutual Reception?	

Mercury's House and Sign attributes that you identify with.

House attributes:

Sign attributes:

Combine the qualities of Mercury's house and sign into a phrase or sentence.

Venus

My Venus is in _____ (sign and symbol) in the _____ House.

	Dignity	Disability
Ruler		
Detriment		
Exaltation		
Fall		
Triplicity		
Term		
Face		
Peregrine		
House Score		
Fast/Slow		
Retrograde/Direct		
Haz		
Oriental/Occident		
Combust/Beams Cazimi		

Partile Aspects?	
Conjunct Fixed Stars?	
House of Joy?	
Dispositor?	
Mutual Reception?	

Venus' House and Sign attributes that you identify with.

House attributes:

Sign attributes:

Combine the qualities of the Venus' house and sign into a phrase or sentence.

Mars

My Mars is in _____ (sign and symbol) in the _____ House.

	Dignity	Disability
Ruler		
Detriment		
Exaltation		
Fall		
Triplicity		
Term		
Face		
Peregrine		
House Score		
Fast/Slow		
Retrograde/Direct		
Haz		
Oriental/Occident		
Combust/Beams Cazimi		

Partile Aspects?	
Conjunct Fixed Stars?	
House of Joy?	
Dispositor?	
Mutual Reception?	

Mars' House and Sign attributes that you identify with.

House attributes:

Sign attributes:

Combine the qualities of the Mars' house and sign into a phrase or sentence.

Jupiter

My Jupiter is in _____ (sign and symbol) in the _____ House.

	Dignity	Disability
Ruler		
Detriment		
Exaltation		
Fall		
Triplicity		
Term		
Face		
Peregrine		
House Score		
Fast/Slow		
Retrograde/Direct		
Haz		
Oriental/Occident		
Combust/Beams Cazimi		

Partile Aspects?	
Conjunct Fixed Stars?	
House of Joy?	
Dispositor?	
Mutual Reception?	

Jupiter's House and Sign attributes that you identify with.

House attributes:

Sign attributes:

Combine the qualities of Jupiter's house and sign into a phrase or sentence.

Saturn

My Saturn is in _____ (sign and symbol) in the _____ House.

	Dignity	Disability
Ruler		
Detriment		
Exaltation		
Fall		
Triplicity		
Term		
Face		
Peregrine		
House Score		
Fast/Slow		
Retrograde/Direct		
Haz		
Oriental/Occident		
Combust/Beams Cazimi		

Partile Aspects?	
Conjunct Fixed Stars?	
House of Joy?	
Dispositor?	
Mutual Reception?	

Saturn's House and Sign attributes that you identify with.

House attributes:

Sign attributes:

Combine the qualities of Saturn's house and sign into a phrase or sentence.

Uranus

My Uranus is in _____ (sign and symbol) in the _____ House.

Notice that Uranus does not have all the dignities and disabilities of the seven planets of the ancients.

	Dignity	Disability
Ruler		
Detriment		
Exaltation		
Fall		
House Score		
Fast/Slow		
Retrograde/Direct		
Haz		
Combust/Beams Cazimi		

Partile Aspects?	
Conjunct Fixed Stars?	
Dispositor?	
Mutual Reception?	

Uranus' House and Sign attributes that you identify with.

House attributes:

Sign attributes:

Combine the qualities of the Uranus' house and sign into a phrase or sentence.

Neptune

My Neptune is in _____ (sign and symbol) in the _____ House.

Neptune does not have all the dignities and disabilities of the seven planets of the ancients.

	Dignity	Disability
Ruler		
Detriment		
Exaltation		
Fall		
House Score		
Fast/Slow		
Retrograde/Direct		
Haz		
Combust/Beams Cazimi		

Partile Aspects?	
Conjunct Fixed Stars?	
Dispositor?	
Mutual Reception?	

Neptune's House and Sign attributes that you identify with.

House attributes:

Sign attributes:

Combine the qualities of Neptune's house and sign into a phrase or sentence.

Pluto

My Pluto is in _____ (sign and symbol) in the _____ House.

Pluto does not have all the dignities and disabilities of the seven planets of the ancients.

	Dignity	Disability
Ruler		
Detriment		
Exaltation		
Fall		
House Score		
Fast/Slow		
Retrograde/Direct		
Haz		
Combust/Beams Cazimi		
Partile Aspects		
Conjunct Fixed Stars		
Dispositor?		
Mutual Reception?		

Partile Aspects?	
Conjunct Fixed Stars?	
Dispositor?	
Mutual Reception?	

Pluto's House and Sign attributes that you identify with.

House attributes:

Sign attributes:

Combine the qualities of Pluto's house and sign into a phrase or sentence.

Chapter 20

Closing

The tables and checklists in this book are the basics. There are progressions, transits, asteroids, and dozen or more techniques to judge a chart. And once you master all that, then there's Vedic astrology with its own set of procedures.

How do I help a Disabled Planet?

Vedic astrology offers sound advice on helping a disabled planet. For example, getting a gemstone for the afflicted planet or saying mantras.

James Braha has a website with the pronunciation of the different planetary mantras. Vedic or Jyotish gemstones can be purchased online. There are other techniques, like making planetary talismans.

Astrological Software

For astrological software, I use Solar Fire. There are several other excellent programs on the market — each one doing something a little bit better than the other programs. I like Solar Fire because the animate tab makes it easy to find favorable times to find planetary elections. Elections are choosing a time when a planet is in the most favorable conditions.

For example, if you want to do a ritual for Venus, I pull up a chart in Solar Fire and select animate. Then I advance the clock one week until Venus is in Taurus, Libra (Rulership), or Pisces. Other factors determine an election and are covered in *Magic of the Planets* (shameless self-promotion).

For a beginner, I recommend using online sources to calculate a chart. Don't invest in software until you know what you want.

The Best Way to Learn Astrology

The best way to learn astrology is to take a class. Look at a person's chart and ask yourself, what stands out? For example, Pluto conjunct the Sun in the fourth house. Obviously, this person is going to have an interesting home life (fourth house). You ask the individual about their home life and listen, really listen, that's where the learning takes place.

Astrology Checklist

	Essential Dignity	Score
1	Rulership	+5
2	Exaltation	+4
3	Triplicity	+3
4	Term	+2
5	Face	+1

The three essential debilities.

	Debility	Score
1	Determent	-5
2	Fall	-4
3	Peregrine	-3

Hayz of Day Planets in a Day Chart						
	Planets above the Horizon in either of these signs					
☉ ♃ ♄	♈	♊	♌	♎	♐	♒

Hayz of Night Planets in a Night Chart						
	Planets above the Horizon in either of these signs					
☽ ♀	♉	♋	♍	♏	♑	♓

For example, Moon in Taurus in a Night Chart and it's above the horizon is in its Hayz.

Hayz of Mars - Night Planet in a Night Chart						
	Mars above the Horizon in either of these signs					
♂	♈	♊	♌	♎	♐	♒

Accidental Dignities			Accidental Debilities	
In the 1st & 10th House	+5		In the 12th House	-5
7th, 4th, and 11th House	+4		8th and 6th House	-2
2nd and 5th House	+3			
9th	+2			
3rd	+1			
Swift in Motion	+2		Slow in Motion	-2
Direct in motion	+4		Retrograde	-4
♂, ♃, ♄ – Oriental	+2		♂, ♃, ♄ – Occidental	-2
☽, ☿, ♀ – Occidental	+2		☿, ♀ – Oriental	-2
☽ increasing	+2		☽ decreasing	-2
Free from combust & ☉ Beams	+5		Combust the Sun	-5
			Under the ☉ Beams	-4
Cazimi	+5			
Partile ☌ with ♃, or ♀	+5		Partile ☌, with ♂ or ♄	-5
Partile △ with ♃ or ♀	+4		Partile ☍ with ♂ or ♄	-4
Partile ✳ with ♃ or ♀	+3		Partile □ with ♂ or ♄	-3
Partile ☌ with ☊	+4		Partile ☌ with ☋	-4
			Besieged by ♂ and ♄	-5
Conjunct Regulus	+6		Conjunct Algol	-5
Conjunct Spica	+5			

196

Made in the USA
Monee, IL
06 June 2022

97526465R20119